A Healing Presence . . .

The Story of Little Company of Mary Hospital's

Journey of Unconditional Love

A Healing Presence . . .

The Story of Little Company of Mary Hospital's

Journey of Unconditional Love

Maurice Possley, Editor

Foreword by Reverend Monsignor Kenneth Velo

R.R. Donnelley & Sons Company

ISBN#: 0-9705160-0-2

R.R. Donnelley & Sons Company
Book Publishing Services
Willard Division
1145 Conwell Avenue
Willard, Ohio 44888

Published by Little Company of Mary Hospital and Health Care Centers
2800 West 95th Street
Evergreen Park, IL 60805

Book staff:

> Author: Little Company of Mary Hospital and Health Care Centers
>
> Editor: Maurice Possley
>
> Typesetting: Regal Graphics, Charlene Herzog
>
> Printer: R.R. Donnelley & Sons Company
>
> Supervisor: Mary Jo May, Executive Director, LCMH Foundation
>
> Consultant: Sister Jean Stickney, L.C.M.
>
> Advisor/Mission: Carol Cassidy Andrews, R.N.
>
> Coordinator: Wendy Drynan

Cover Illustration:

> Photographs: Sisters arrive for laying of the cornerstone of the Hospital, April 14, 1929.
> The window pictured represents the three pioneering Little Company of Mary Sisters who first came to America, Mother Mary Veronica, Mother Mary Patrick and Mother Mary Philomena.

Acknowledgments

For more than a century, the strength and faith of the founding sisters and the love and loyalty of their friends and companions have been a beacon to us all. As they labored and prayed together, so, too, is this book the result of a collaborative effort. It is impossible to list the name of every person who contributed to the prose and photographs that have helped bring the Little Company Sisters and their Hospital to life in these pages. However, some stand out.

Carol Andrews, whose wide network of relationships dating from when she was a nursing student and continuing today, was instrumental in ferreting out wonderful stories from the Sisters, physicians and friends. Sister Jean Stickney, L.C.M., in carrying out the legacy of Mary Potter in her heart every day, helped find just the right words in important places. Mary Jo May and the Foundation Board of Directors offered a well-spring of support. Denise Stillman provided expert proofreading and a sense of style. Joan Murphy and the Public Relations staff, Mary Lou Durkin, Steve Hallenbeck, Gloria Jackson, Marty McLaughlin, Sharon Pisoni, Mary Jo Quick and Eileen Sauser, contributed their time and expertise.

Special thanks goes to Sister Kathleen McIntyre, L.C.M., for her leadership of this project.

Countless others – Little Company's Sisters, physicians, nurses, administration and volunteers, neighbors and friends – helped search out and identify photographs and offered advice. Their shared memories – some of which were not used due to constraints on space – are a treasure.

Charlene Herzog and the staff of Regal Graphics were tireless in carefully preparing the archived pictures and text for publication. The American Province of the Little Company of Mary Sisters, Dr. James West and the Hospital's Professional Staff provided the financial support necessary to create "A Healing Presence . . . The Story of Little Company of Mary Hospital's Journey of Unconditional Love."

Most significantly, this book would not have been possible without the effort of Wendy Drynan, whose untiring work, enthusiasm, good humor, and endless supply of patience kept the process on course and on time.

For all who had a hand in making this book possible, I thank you on behalf of the Sisters and all who have entered Little Company's doors.

– Maurice Possley, Editor

Foreword

"Where were you born?"
"Evergreen Park."
"So was I. Little Company of Mary."

"What hospital is your sister in?"
"Little Company."
"That's our hospital, too."

"Where do you work?"
"Little Company of Mary."
"So does my aunt."

So many of our conversations have begun with South Side geography and, in particular, an anchoring institution extremely vital to the community – so important to each of us.

Some remember the four-floor hospital that was initially built. Others recall the long driveway to the emergency entrance on the west side of the building. Still others, the elm-lined entranceway that formed a canopy to the main door from 95th Street.

Some remember stitches or a cast in an antiseptic-white basement wing. Others remember nurses' stations that served as hubs at the center of the four wings on every floor.

Although I can't remember the day I was born, I do recall countless visits. Perhaps the most memorable was to the emergency room after my brother bashed me with a wooden stool at age five.

More than buildings and trees, wings and emergency rooms – at the core of the hospital are dedicated people. And the heart of those people are the distinctively blue-veiled Sisters whose recognizable presence has been the balm for many a wound.

The Sisters began this work with the doctors, nurses, technicians and staff who ensured life and breath to a caring and healing endeavor. To the fortune of many, this legacy of wellness has been upheld by their successors throughout the decades.

"Little Comp" towers high, yet with gripping roots. Across its threshold – whether emergency, main door or outpatient – tens of thousands of people have sought and found healing and compassion here.

And when you seek healing, you seek God whether you know it or not.

On behalf of those who have found God beneath Mary's tenth-floor motherly mantle, under which all are

protected, we pour out our gratitude to the members of her Little Company. Allow this book to rest on your coffee table and be visited often. Let the pages of history enlighten you, the words of praise inspire you, and the deeds so graciously given encourage you.

As this book's title reminds us, Little Company of Mary retains a healing presence and continues a journey of unconditional love. Return that love.

They have enabled life for so many of us. Now, allow these pages to bring their ongoing story to life.

Monsignor Velo

Reverend Monsignor Kenneth Velo
President
Catholic Extension

Table of Contents

Introduction

Venerable Mary Potter

Mary Potter was born November 22, 1847, in London, one of five children of William Norwood and Mary Anne Martin Potter. Her mother, an Anglican, had been received into the Catholic Church two years earlier.

Educated in a small Catholic private boarding school, Mary acknowledged a calling to Religious Life in 1869, breaking off her engagement to Godfrey King. Ironically, King initially had believed Mary was lacking spirituality and had given her a number of books to read on the subject. On July 30 of that year, she began her first year as a postulant of the Mercy Order. On December 8, 1868, Mary took the name of Sister Mary Aloysius and began her novitiate year. But nearly two years later, Mary was stricken with poor health and returned to her home on June 23, 1870, to recover. She was so ill that she was confined to her home for much of the entire next year.

Toward the end of 1871, during personal prayer, Mary began to experience a need to care for the sick and dying and pray for them. In 1872, she made the Solemn Act by which she consecrated her whole self, her entire life, and all she possessed to Jesus through Mary. She felt impelled to invite other women to join her and to dedicate themselves to this ministry.

The Statue of the Little Company of Mary at the Foot of the Cross

Five years later, in Hyson-Green, Nottingham, England, Mother Mary Potter and five companions acquired an abandoned stocking factory and founded a new religious Order dedicated to the care of the sick and the dying.

Inspired by Mary, the Mother of Jesus, and the little company of faithful followers who remained at the foot of the cross at Calvary to support her as her Son was dying, the Order was to be the Sisters of the Little Company of Mary. At Calvary, the Mercy of God poured out upon mankind. By uniting themselves in a special way to the mystery of Calvary, the Sisters of the Little Company of Mary would honor that outpouring. They dedicated themselves to the assistance of all Christ's suffering people, most particular, to the poorest of the poor, the sick and the dying. Mary Potter was a visionary, recognizing even then the value of holistic health – the physical, spiritual and emotional well being of the individual.

The last quarter of the 19th century was a time of great upheaval and conflict. The world was filled with poverty, illness and a struggle for survival on many levels. Mary Potter was aware of the evils that humans inflict upon each other and witnessed its impact on men, women and children who lived without love, compassion or caring. In response, prayer and presence became the hallmark of the Little Company of Mary.

Since the beginning, no matter what endeavors the Sisters have undertaken, all have been bound to pray for the sick and dying of the world. The Sisters remain constantly aware of global concerns and hold all peoples up to the Father, imploring His mercy upon them, especially those who do not know of the 'good news' of Jesus, and those who live in pain.

Venerable Mary Potter dreamed that one day the world would be made one in Christ. To that end, she devoted her life. She did not limit herself to any one apostolate. Rather, she knew that the mission of the Church was to bring all people together. Later, in one of her published works, she wrote, "By uniting themselves with Mary, and by giving all into her hands, the Sisters of this Little Company of Mary would bring to the world a way of finding and loving Christ – a 'little' way of simplicity and compassion."

As Foundress, Venerable Mary Potter always had a very special and personal love for her own Sisters. She nurtured her "Little Company" with the care and vigilance of a true mother. This loving care was constant and persevering despite her weakness and ill health. Her faith and courage were tested. She battled her own illnesses and struggled to find the resources to bring hope and healing to those in need.

In 1882, she traveled to Rome and met with Pope Leo XIII to ask him to bless her Order and work in England, which by then had expanded to four convents. To her surprise, His Holiness replied, "Why go back? Why not remain? The doors of Rome are open to you." And so she did, opening a convent there two years later.

Expansion continued. In 1885, the Sisters sent a delegation to Sydney, Australia, and in 1886 they opened a foundation in Florence, Italy. The following year, at the invitation of Count Moore of Moresford, Tipperary, Mother Mary took over a Hospital in Limerick, Ireland.

The relationship of the Little Company of Mary Sisters and the City of Chicago evolved in the early 1890s when Charles A. Mair, a Chicago businessman who frequently traveled abroad, journeyed along with his wife to Italy. While in Rome, Mrs. Mair became terminally ill and was entrusted to the care of the Sisters of the Little Company of Mary Calvary Hospital there. Mr. Mair was so impressed with the efforts of the Sisters that he invited them to come to Chicago.

On April 26, 1893, three Sisters wearing the pale blue veils of the Order of the Little Company of Mary Sisters boarded the steam ship *Kaiser Wilhelm* in Genoa, Italy. They embarked upon a journey of

unconditional love, guided by a shared vision and strengthened by a collective will.

These unlikely pioneers, Mother Mary Veronica, Mother Mary Patrick and Mother Mary Philomena, headed across the Atlantic to New York City to begin a ministry in America. The women were armed with an abundance of courage, faith and prayer as well as the inspiration of Venerable Mary Potter, Foundress of the Little Company of Mary.

"As we steamed out of the harbour," Mother Mary Veronica later wrote, "The little trio stood on deck, looking with tearful eyes at Mother Mary Philip and Mother Mary Cecilia as they stood on shore waving their handkerchiefs until they became lost in the distance. Then, indeed, we felt quite alone!"

It was a journey that was months in the making and marked a new dawn for the Little Company of Mary Order that was less than two decades old. And so it was on May 9, 1893, Mother Mary Veronica, Mother Mary Patrick and Mother Mary Philomena sailed into New York Harbor after 15 days at sea.

Mother Mary Veronica recalled their arrival in her diary. "Shortly after the tender drew up, we received a most cordial letter of 'Welcome to America' from our good benefactor, Mr. Mair, telling us his agent would meet us when we landed, which he did – handing us another letter from Mr. Mair with our tickets to Chicago."

On May 12, upon their arrival in Chicago, their train was met by Mr. Mair, who drove them to the Auditorium Hotel. It was four years to the day that the Sisters had begun to nurse his wife in Rome. "We were hardly settled in our rooms when a reporter for one of the papers sent a note asking us to kindly tell what connection we had with the Vatican, and from what part of Rome did we come?" Mother Mary Veronica wrote, "We went off to rest, thinking how smart those Americans are, looking for news the morning people arrive."

Charles A. Mair

Sisters sitting outside in the yard behind the old convent at 41st Street and Indiana Avenue.
The Sisters designated by number are shown prior to their mission to Argentina.

1 Mother M Patrick
2 Mother M Columba
3 Sister M. Philome
4 Sister M.Raphael
5 Sister M. Rita

After early Mass at St. Mary's Church on South Wabash Avenue and breakfast at the hotel, Mr. Mair arrived and took them to their future convent. True to his promise, Mr. Mair had provided a home at 4130 South Indiana Avenue, where they quickly moved in and established the Order's first Little Company of Mary convent on American soil.

"The place looked most deplorably dirty inside – and out,"Mother Mary Veronica declared. Undeterred, they began to work immediately. On the following Monday they began venturing about the city, purchasing a stove and kitchen utensils. So began their ministry.

They mastered getting on and off streetcars and learned how to light a coal stove. They rolled up their sleeves and scoured their new home. By May 30 – 18 days after arriving in Chicago – the first Mass was said in the convent. As the requests for nursing care began to appear, the Sisters responded by visiting their homes to minister and heal at their bedsides, serving their patients through care, prayer and a compassionate presence – the forerunner of today's hospice care.

Before her death in 1998, Sister Nancy Boyle, L.C.M., recalled, "Even with Mr. Mair's consistent support, the early years were difficult for the first

Sisters. Their early accommodations were sparse; there were few Sisters and so many who needed their care; and the Sisters were in a strange land. The simplest of tasks were challenging, but the Sisters' good humor eased their frustration."

Frequently, the Sisters left their convent to nurse the sick on Sunday evenings and did not return to their convent until Friday. They undertook the care of the patient's entire family, cooking meals and overseeing the care of any children in the home. Their approach always was family oriented.

On December 3, 1896, work began on the Sisters' new chapel in honor of the Maternal Heart of Mary and in memory of Mr. Mair's wife, Cornelia. By the time the first Mass was held the following May, the community in America had expanded to eight Sisters.

"We are always very busy," wrote one of the Sisters in her journal in 1899. "The more the Sisters are known, the more they are sought after, and knowing their nursing so well, they are a great help to doctors and patients, besides looking after the souls of those under their care."

Mr. Mair continued to serve as their benefactor and financial advisor until his death in 1915. Although the Sisters faced many hardships, they were empowered by their faith and a vision that gave them strength and courage. Their expanding mission of unconditional love grew and flourished.

More than a century ago, Venerable Mary Potter rejoiced in God's love, trusted completely in His power at work within her and strove simply to do His will. Little Company of Mary Hospital and Health Care Centers is the embodiment of a woman who was a beacon of hope with a burning desire to bring the world to Christ through Mary.

Her legacy continues.

First convent of the Little Company of Mary Sisters at 4130 South Indiana Avenue

"Mary Potter's 'little' way of simplicity and compassion continues today not only because of the Sisters, but also because of the generosity of the men and women who believe in her vision and mission and have accepted it as part of their lives. All of you are part of the 'Greater Company of Mary' which Mary Potter started in the early days, when she realized that there was so much to do and that the Sisters couldn't do it alone. We are blessed because you help to make visible the healing presence of Jesus in your daily living. Our ministry is richer because of you and we thank you."

"May you have Peace and Love in your Hearts and in your Families."

— Sister Carol Pacini, L.C.M., Provincial Leader

"We have been called by God, we have come, then we are past, wither? And for what? We know not, but whatever work we are given, we must remember we are sent.

Go forth . . . the whole world is your domain. Go forth into all nations. The God of Mary will be with you."

— Venerable Mary Potter
(Conf. "N"; MC14)

1930s

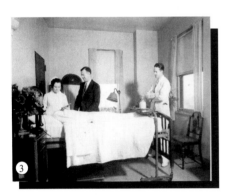

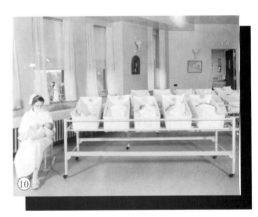

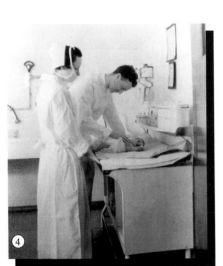

1 - Future site of Little Company of Mary Hospital. 2 - Blessing of the Cornerstone. 3 - Early patient room.
4 - Donald Madden, M.D., examines newborn. 5 - Sisters arrive at dedication, 1930. 6 - Our legacy of care begins! 7 - Nursing students in 1936.
8 - Aerial view of completed four-story Tower Building. 9 - Front Entrance. 10 - Nursery. 11 - Going home with newborn baby.

Chapter 1
The Beginning
1930-1939

"In the afternoon, Mother M. Stanislaus and Mother M. Dorothea, with some professed Sisters went to 95th and California to be present at the ceremony of breaking ground for the new Hospital. There were six priests present and quite a few of the Auxiliary members. The architect and contractor looked very important there. Father Hurley had not yet arrived to bless the ground, so Father Croke from St. Cecilia's blessed it instead and dug up the first shovel full. Mother M. Stanislaus dug the second shovel full. The photographers were busy all this time. We must have made a picture in the snow, which was gently falling at the time and had been ever since early morning. Some said it meant luck.

After a few minutes, Father Hurley appeared on the scene and was persuaded to bless the ground again, which he did - but the digging part he left to the other priests. As soon as the photographers had put away their cameras, all the Sisters and Auxiliary members dug up a shovel full. The big steam shovel, which had been close by watching our poor endeavors, began and made a swoop down

February 6, 1929 - Ground Breaking

into the earth and brought up a large quantity of dirt and flung it to one side at some distance. It was interesting to watch it, but it was too cold to remain standing for long, so we left for home. All came to 4130 Indiana, where the visitors had some light refreshment."

– From the Sisters' Log Book February 6, 1929

The morning of February 6, 1929, had indeed, dawned very cold and damp. Mother Mary Stanislaus, Mother Mary Dorothea and Mother Mary Dunstan hardly noticed the frigid weather. With spirits high, they led that contingent of Sisters to 95th Street and California Avenue to see the realization of a dream – a four-story, 150-bed Hospital.

It was an exciting new phase in the Sisters' ministry in America. The Hospital was the result of a dramatic increase in the demands on the Sisters in the 1920s. The Order of the blue-veiled Sisters dreamed what – for some – appeared to be an impossible dream: continuing their ministry through construction of a hospital. Fortified by their faith that nothing is impossible with God, the Sisters forged ahead.

It was a bold decision backed by the evolution of medical science toward safer sterilization techniques, surgery and anesthesia. Nurses no longer depended on pneumonia jackets and camphorated oil rubs to treat respiratory ailments.

"I remember attending the ground breaking for the hospital. It was a long, cold walk from the Western Avenue streetcar to California Avenue."

– Robert P. O'Malley First cousin to Sister Kathleen McIntyre, L.C.M.

1

Original site for Little Company of Mary Hospital on 95th Street when it was just an empty prairie

In a hospital, patients could avail themselves of techniques not accessible to the Sisters as they treated patients in their homes.

The nucleus of the Hospital building fund had been established in 1925 when Mrs. Charles Mair, the second wife of Charles Mair, died and left her estate to the Little Company of Mary Order. Her daughter-in-law, Mrs. George McLaughlin, became head of a committee to raise money for the Hospital. Grateful former patients and friends of the Sisters worked diligently as members of the Auxiliary formed in 1926 to raise funds.

Finally, on April 24, 1927, the Sisters of the Little Company of Mary purchased the land from the Triezenberg family for $60,000. Some observers regarded the purchase as folly. The land was in the middle of nowhere. There were only about 1,600 people living in the area at the time. Who would support a hospital? Where would the patients come from? These were important questions, but ones that would be dealt with through faith and hard work.

The deep faith of Mother M. Stanislaus, Mother M. Dunstan and Mother M. Dorothea and their unwavering commitment to the sick and dying had brought them to this juncture; construction of a Hospital to continue their ministry was about to begin.

Even as the steam shovel was turning the soil, the fundraising continued. In the spring of 1929, a group of women formed a city-wide organization to raise funds to build the Hospital. Mrs. McLaughlin headed the group with Vice-Chairman Miss Mayme Joyce. The Auxiliary of the Little Company of Mary was now 900 strong. An event took place at Orchestra Hall on Easter Monday night in 1929, and featured opera singer Edith Mason, a member of the Chicago Civic Opera Company. The Sisters participated in this fundraising event by selling bonds to build the Hospital.

Major funding also was sought from industrial and manufacturing giants, such as South Works, a steel-making facility on Chicago's South Side that later became known as U.S. Steel. The Sisters contacted George Ferry, a supervisor at South Works, who championed the Sisters' cause and helped persuade the company to make a substantial donation. In return, the Sisters agreed always to make beds available to injured workers in need of care. Other major companies followed suit.

Nine weeks after the ground breaking, the cornerstone was laid on April 14, 1929. Bishop Sheil, with assistance from priests from nearby parishes, blessed the cornerstone. The Reverend E.S. Keough, Pastor of Holy Rosary Church in Pullman, preached an eloquent sermon. The Boy Scout band from St. Michael's parish in Chicago provided music for all those assembled. Included were representatives from various religious Orders and hundreds of people from the community.

April 14, 1929 – Dedication Day

Cornerstone hoisted in place

Blessing of the cornerstone

May 1 - Hospital under construction

August 27 - Hospital under construction

On January 19, 1930, the dream became reality as Little Company of Mary Hospital opened its doors with a staff consisting of seven doctors and 50 employees. The formal dedication took place at 3 p.m. Mother M. Stanislaus, Mother M. Dorothea and Mother M. Dunstan, the three Sisters who established Little Company of Mary Hospital, were the first administrators.

The original structure of Little Company of Mary Hospital

"I was a page boy at the dedication of the hospital. There were flashes of light, probably from the cameras, which startled me and when I stood up to try to get away, I leaned on the Cardinal's legs."

– Donald Koflin

His Eminence Cardinal Mundelein officiated and Bishop Bernard Sheil blessed the site. Numerous priests and about 3,000 lay people attended the open house that followed. The 150-bed four-story brick building was designed by Joseph McCarthy in northern Italian style architecture and was built in the shape of the cross which also allowed each patient room to have sunlight and fresh air. The main lobby of the original structure was a showplace of its time with ornate plasterwork, inlaid terrazzo floors and beautiful carved furniture. The Hospital's outside was buff-colored brick with limestone trim.

Main Floor Lobby

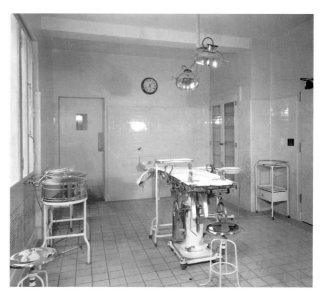

Operating Room

Hospital kitchen

Visitors entered through a portico of glass and tile that stretched over a curved driveway. The coat of arms of the Archdiocese of Chicago was carved in stone over the entrance. The Sisters were in charge of the operating rooms, x-ray, pharmacy and diet kitchen. Also they comprised the entire nursing staff.

Baby goes home

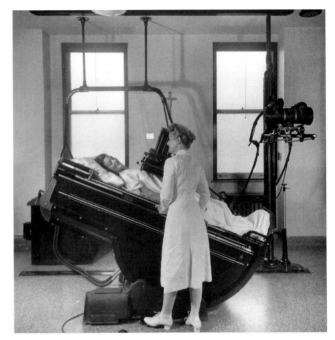

X-Ray Machine

Ambulance with Joseph Cummings at the wheel

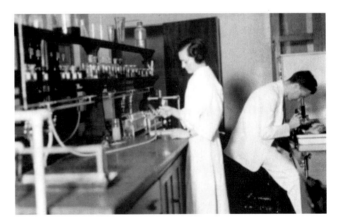

Surrounded by beakers, test tubes and Bunsen burners, Dr. Donald Madden looks through a microscope.

1930 - (left to right)
Dr. J.J. Moore, Mother M. Stanislaus Madigan, L.C.M., Mother Dorothea Dwight, L.C.M. and Dr. Tobin

Five of the original 33 Sisters at Little Company of Mary Hospital
(left to right) Sister M. Agnes O'Neill, L.C.M., Sister M. Catherine Barrett, L.C.M.,
Sister M. Ignatius Dooley, L.C.M., Sister M. Leo Lang, L.C.M. and Sister M. Hilda O'Halloran, L.C.M.

On January 21, 1930, the very first patient was admitted. On January 23, two more patients were admitted; on January 24, the first baby, Douglas Kier of La Porte, Indiana, was born at Little Company. He weighed a healthy nine pounds.

January 24, 1930 - Douglas Kier being held by Nurse Margaret Casey

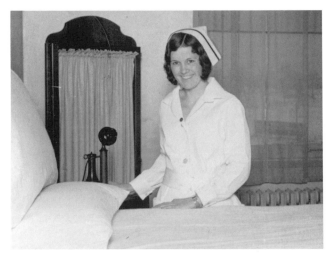

Typical patient room in men's ward

In those early days, the Sisters overcame financial difficulties through untold sacrifice and extraordinary efforts. Few people lived close to the Hospital and it was difficult to reach without an automobile. The patients were few. Being innovative caregivers even then, the Sisters cleverly placed the only two patients in rooms across from each other so that when they looked across the hall, they saw an occupied bed. Often, the lights of the Hospital glowed in vacant rooms facing 95th Street to give the impression that all the patient beds were occupied.

Bedside manner

The hub of activity on each floor was a rotunda area that served as the nurses' station. The women's ward was pleasant but without many amenities. By year's end, a total of 1,391 patients had been admitted; 232 babies had been born; and staff physicians had handled 554 surgeries and 359 emergencies.

Seeing the need for well educated nurses, the Sisters began plans for the Little Company of Mary Hospital School of Nursing in 1931. The school was approved by the Department of Registration and Education and fully accredited by the National League for Nursing Education. The first six graduates, each a Little Company of Mary Sister, received their cherished diplomas in 1934.

Soon Little Company became the heart of medical activity in the rapidly expanding southwest suburban area. Medical research began to accelerate at an unprecedented rate. Improvements in patient care procedures and facilities followed in rapid succession. Meanwhile, the population increased and the community of Evergreen Park expanded. Little Company of Mary Hospital kept pace with all of these moving forces, recognizing the needs of the community it served, especially during the Depression years.

In January of 1935, when Little Company celebrated its fifth birthday, the Hospital reported that 12 percent of its service was rendered at no cost to patients and that 43 percent of the Hospital's patients paid only nominal charges.

At the same time, dedicated community residents directed their efforts in the best interests of the Hospital and formed the Senior Service Club. They rolled bandages and packaged materials for sterilization, held bake sales and participated in numerous social functions to raise funds for the Hospital. Shortly thereafter, Sister Magdalen Nolan

Statue given to the Sisters in 1928 by the Auxiliary
Front: Sister Rosarii Hassett, Sister Callista Donaghue, Mother M. Dunstan Kelleher, Sister Thaddeus Brennan,
Mother M. Stanislaus Madigan, Sister Evangelist Tuohy, Sister Leo Lang
Back: Sister de Lourdes Lee, Mother M. Dorothea Dwight

"Red Ormsby, a professional baseball umpire who lived in Evergreen Park, was a patient at LCM for quite awhile. He kept mentioning his horse. A student — taking to heart the Nursing School lesson of caring not only physically, but also emotionally and spiritually as well — walked over to Mr. Ormsby's barn on 97th Street, saddled the horse and rode down 95th Street. Mr. Ormsby was put in a wheelchair and brought to the front lawn so he could have a visit with his horse. The student was my mother, Fran Keating, Class of 1938."

— Marie Moore, Human Resources

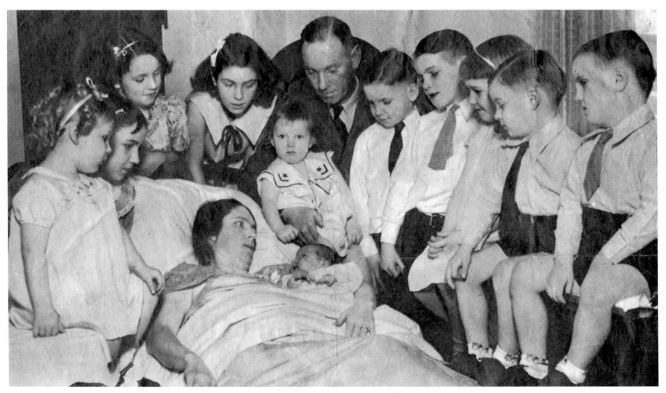

Mr. and Mrs. "Red" Ormsby and family

formed the Junior Service Club to support the maternity department of the Hospital. Eventually these volunteer groups became part of the Hospital's Auxiliary.

The Auxiliary continued its fundraising work. A benefit performance of the Abbey Theater Players of Dublin was held on January 28 and 29, 1935, at the Harris Theater. Funds materialized in other ways too. In April 1939, the late Mrs. Ellen Donovan left her entire estate to the Hospital where she had been a patient before her death at age 88.

Little Company's first decade of service came to an end as the world was in turmoil. World War II was about to begin and Little Company would face a staff shortage as many of its doctors and nurses went to war in service of their country.

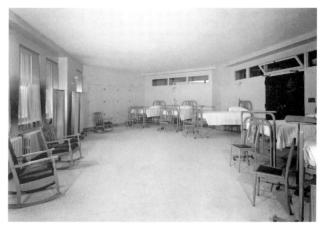

Typical ward

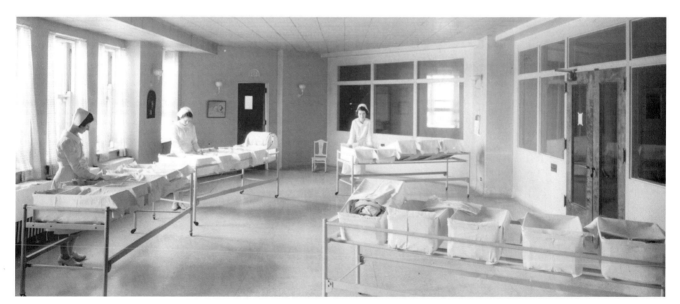

Nursery

Winter scene of the Hospital at night

"The singing men of steel from the South Works steel plant sang at the Hospital every year at Christmas. They made appearances on every floor at Little Company."
— Edward Madden
Retired South Works Supervisor

"Raphael," a Russian Wolf Hound, belonged to Mother Dorothea

The Hospital's first Auxiliary

"In 1934, when I was four years old, my brother was in the Hospital for more than six weeks. I was royally entertained inside the offices of Mother Stanislaus and Mother Dunstan. This was more than 60 years ago and I've been involved ever since. Last year, I received my 50-year service pin."

— Sister Joseph Casey, L.C.M.

"I was nine years old at the time the Hospital was being built and when it opened its doors to the community. As kids we were very impressed by the four-story building with something we had never heard about before — an automated elevator. They had to get the older kids in the neighborhood, the 12- and 13-year-olds, to operate the elevators because the adults of the time, like my parents who were in their prime, were hesitant of pushing a button to make an elevator go without having someone in there turning wheels and handles."

— Martin Ozinga, Jr.

1940s

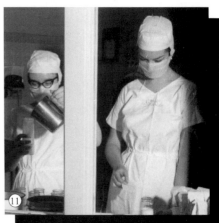

1 - Nurses residence, 1945. 2 - Pediatrics Outpatient Clinic. 3 - Sterilizing supplies. 4 - Main entrance at night.
5 - The Gray Ladies, fr om Beverly, our first volunteers. 6 - Final floors added to Tower Building, 1949.
7 - Nurse and nurse cadet graduating class in the 40s. 8 - Hospital Day, 1942. 9 - 10th Anniversary Mass, 1940.
10 - Sisters outside main entrance of Hospital, late 1940s. 11 - Fourth floor Formula Room, early 1940s.

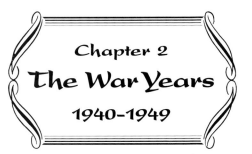

Chapter 2
The War Years
1940-1949

"During World War II, gas rationing limited driving. If we were walking to the Hospital and wearing white shoes and stockings, many drivers would offer us a ride. Mother Dorothea was director of the School of Nursing. She wanted 'her girls' to be ready for the battlefield, so she hired drill sergeants from Morgan Park Military Academy to put us through our paces. The drills were held every Saturday afternoon on the front lawn."

— *Mary Jane O'Sullivan, R.N.*

Physicians' Awards Dinner
Sisters served doctors at the annual dinner

On January 19, 1940, as the Hospital celebrated its 10th anniversary, the rapid growth of the suburban population and its increasing demand on the facility prompted discussion of further expansion.

In May of 1944, as the War continued, the Sisters responded to the increasing need for nurses. At the time, 118 students were in training, and War requirements pushed the total need to 150. During this time, classes were held in the sub-basement of the Hospital, and there was a pressing demand for a nurses' residence.

The Sisters respond to the increasing need for nurses.

1945 - Student Nurse Cadets

1943 - First Red Cross Nurses Aide Class Graduates

"It was November 20, 1941, and while my husband Frank attended Thanksgiving Day services at Evergreen Park Christian Reformed Church, I was at home anxiously awaiting the arrival of my second child. My baby was not, however, going to patiently wait for Daddy's return, and Frank had to rush home early from the service leaving the congregation to pray for a safe delivery. Although my baby interrupted one religious celebration, we were in time for another. Cardinal Stritch paid a Thanksgiving Day visit to the Hospital and gave his blessing to all the newborn babies, including my son Marty Frank. The family always felt Marty got off to such a good start because he had both church communities welcoming him into the world with their prayers."

– Grace Ozinga

The in-service Hospital volunteers, a group of women from Beverly known as the "Gray Ladies,"
became part of the Little Company of Mary family.

"I became a Gray Lady volunteer through the

Red Cross during World War II and was sent

to Little Company to do volunteer work. I

worked for Mother Dorothea."

— Ruth Radke, Gray Ladies

Dr. L. Langdon

Dr. A. Ross

Dr. F. Ross

Dr. J. Young

Our Staff Proudly Served

H. Concor and M. Lane

Dr. R. Hogan

Dr. D. Sullivan

Dr. D.J. Madden

"On our first date, I wound up at Little Company of Mary Hospital. Mike, a Chicagoan, talked me, a Lockport girl, into going to the Hospital to visit his two-year-old sister Peggy, who was so very sick. He ducked behind the columns so she wouldn't see him and cry to go home."

— Jean McGonigal, Volunteer

They served . . .

. . . and they wed

In the fall, construction on the Nurses' residence began one block west of the Hospital between Mozart Street and Francisco Avenue. In November of 1945, the facility opened, providing living quarters, classrooms, a library and recreational facilities for 175 student nurses.

The Nursing School was affiliated with DePaul University, which sent professors to instruct the students in Evergreen Park. Mother M. Dorothea was director of the School of Nursing and Margaret Crowe was assistant director. Students attended classes during the day and usually worked six days a week on the evening or night shifts. It was a demanding schedule but provided invaluable clinical experience.

September 1944 – Nurses' residence ground breaking

September 1944 – Nurses residence ground breaking

"Sister Imelda played cupid, introducing me to Dr. James F. Graham. She checked on our romance over the next year and was so happy when we were married. Sisters Imelda, Francis and Camille conspired together so we would have our days off together. We were very fortunate."

– Loretta Graham, R.N., Class of 1947

"When I was four, Dr. Richard Lawler removed my appendix. My sobbing mother was taken in hand by the Sisters, hugged and comforted by endless cups of tea and sandwiches. She also was allowed to stay with me overnight."

– Rose Lamb, Auxilian

School of Nursing

Little Company of Mary Sisters gather in the front of the Hospital's main entrance.

The School was limited to accepting 70 to 75 students each year and as its reputation grew, young women eagerly sought admission. The three-year course leading to the nursing diploma was designed, through classroom instruction and supervised practice, to prepare the student to care for the sick, to promote health and to help fight disease. Emphasis was placed upon the patient as an individual, as a member of a family and as a citizen of the community and stressed the importance of the psychological, spiritual and social aspects of healing.

*May 1947 – Mary Jane O'Sullivan (right)
first day as a graduate nurse*

"The Senior Service Club was an outstanding group of women who folded bandages for us every Tuesday. In those days, everything was reused. Bandages were washed, sterilized and folded."

— *Mary Jane O'Sullivan, R.N.*

```
                                No. 200
      JUNIOR SERVICE CLUB
             of
 LITTLE COMPANY OF MARY HOSPITAL

     CHRISTMAS CABARET DANCE
             at
THE MERCHANTS and MANUFACTURERS CLUB
        MERCHANDISE MART

    CHUCK CAVALLO and ORCHESTRA
SATURDAY
DECEMBER 18, 1948              ADMISSION
NINE TIL ONE                     $5.00
```

December 18, 1948, ticket to Christmas Cabaret Dance

Upon successful completion of the three-year course, the school pin and diploma were conferred on the new graduates who were now eligible to take the State Board Examination for Registered Nurses.

The Little Company of Mary School of Nursing pin is round with a blue border and gold letters. A raised sword-pierced heart and a lily are engraved on a gold center. The border signifies the blue of our Lady and the Sisters of Little Company of Mary. The lily signifies purity and the sword represents the seven sorrows of the Immaculate Heart of Mary.

"The bus service on 95th street was not always on schedule. In the winter, we froze. Sister Helena saw we were numb from the cold and she made toast and coffee for each one of us individually. She cared for her nurses. We worked 7 a.m. to 7 p.m. split shifts with time off in the middle of the day. During those hours, we played cards in the basement."

— Marie Haslouer Peterlin, R.N.

1943 – Capping Day

1946 – Nursing students
Mary Jane O'Sullivan, Lil O'Connor Barry,
Shirley Zilligen Kass, Dorothy Scully Schaffer,
Rosemary Angrten Johnson

1945 – Betty Ahlers DeTamble
at Capping Ceremony

Class of 1947 – School of Nursing Graduation

"I loved going into Mother Dunstan's office and talking to her parrot. I also enjoyed going on rounds with my father, Dr. Donald Farmer, because I would wait at the nursing stations and they would give me candy."

– Madonna Abdishi

Dr. Donald Farmer

Following World War II and during the ensuing Baby Boom, Little Company of Mary played a major role. In one month alone – July of 1946 – four sets of twins were born within 10 days. As a result, the 70 cribs in the nursery were full. Once again the Sisters showed their creativity: one evening, when the obstetrics nurse arrived with a set of twins to find that all the bassinets were filled, wash-basins were collected and then padded to accommodate the newest of the newborns.

Dr. Wm. Hagstrom, Dr. R. Cummings,
Dr. P. McNulty, Dr. W. Furey, Dr. Paul Headland,
Dr. Edmund Lawler, Dr. Frank Lawler
and Dr. Paul Lawler

"Another memory is the 'Baby Boom' years in the late 1940s and 1950s. Meeting this tremendous rise in infant births was responsible for the development of newborn and premature care. The Baby Boom challenged creative energies in those days. For example, we created a great air conditioning unit by placing large tubs with cakes of ice and using large fans to blow over the ice and cool off the nursery environment. When faced with a shortage of beds when the census grew, we turned to Burney Bros. bread boxes and made very usable and temporary cribs. It was a time of teamwork – working long hours and being very happy in our work. It was a time when Sunday afternoon became a preferred tour of duty as professional photographers came to take pictures of the infants and our own portfolios were kept filled with 'shots' of us – our families and friends were inundated with our pictures."

– Sister Magdalen Nolan, L.C.M.

"My mother, Mary Carroll, always treasured her years as an Army nurse and her training at Little Company. Beyond the love of her family, my mother treasured nothing more than the friendships she built through the years in Chicago."

– Tim Carroll

Mary Carroll, R.N.

The Cost for Care at Little Company of Mary Hospital in the 1940s

Bills Payable on Presentation (1 week in advance)
Not responsible for valuables unless checked at office
Doctor's bills not included in this statement.

May 17 19 49

M Lawrence Eurkaitis   Room No. 615-1

LITTLE COMPANY OF MARY HOSPITAL
EVERGREEN PARK, ILL.

Report Any Inaccuracies At Office Promptly

	Amount	Credit	Balance
STATEMENT RENDERED			
BOARD & ROOM	3 00		
NURSERY			
DELIVERY ROOM & ANAESTHETIC			
OPERATING ROOM & ANAESTHETIC	18 00		
BLOOD BANK			
DRESSINGS			
MEDICINE	20		
TELEPHONE & TELEGRAPH			
LABORATORY	2 00	PAID	
X-RAY			
SPLINT			
CAST	LITTLE COMPANY OF MARY HOSPITAL		
TREATMENTS, ETC.			
SUNDRIES	23 00		
EMERGENCY			

Copies of Hospital Bills Provided by Former Patients

LITTLE COMPANY OF MARY HOSPITAL
EVERGREEN PARK 42, ILLINOIS

NAME Conway, Mrs. Julia   ROOM NO.   RATE 7.00
ADDRESS 8129 S. Bishop
CITY Chicago, Ill.

MEMO	LINE	DATE	DESCRIPTION	CHARGES	CREDITS	BALANCE
	1	DEC 29-49	LABORATORY	★ 4.00		★ 4.00
	2	Dec 29-49	Drugs	3.55		
	3	Dec 29-49	Del. Room	18.00		
	4	Dec 29-49	Anesthesia	10.00		36.10
	5	Dec 29-49	Drugs	.55		
	6	DEC 30-49	ROOM	★ 7.00		
	7	DEC 30-49	NURSERY	★ 3.50		★ 46.60
	8	DEC 30-49	DRUGS	★ 2.00		★ 48.60
	9	DEC 31-49	ROOM	★ 7.00		
	10	DEC 31-49	NURSERY	★ 3.50		★ 59.10
	11	DEC 31-49	MISCELL.	A★ 0.30		★ 59.40
	12	JAN-1-50	ROOM	★ 7.00		
	13	JAN-1-50	NURSERY	★ 3.50		★ 69.90
	14	JAN-1-50	MISCELL.	A★ 0.10		★ 70.00
	15	JAN-2-50	ROOM	★ 7.00		
	16	JAN-2-50	NURSERY	★ 3.50		★ 80.50
	17	JAN-2-50	MISCELL.	A★ 0.20		80.70
	18	JAN-2-50	DRUGS	★ 2.25		★ 82.95
	19	JAN-2-50	MISCELL.	A★ 0.43		★ 83.38
	20	JAN-3-50	ROOM	★ 7.00		
	21	JAN-3-50	NURSERY	★ 3.50		★ 93.88
	22	JAN-3-50	MISCELL.	A★ 0.20		★ 94.08
	23	JAN-4-50	ROOM	★ 7.00		
	24	JAN-4-50	NURSERY	★ 3.50		104.58

ROOM RENT PAYABLE 1 WEEK IN ADVANCE
BLUE CROSS NO.

CODE:
A	TELEPHONE	D	SUNDRIES	G—CH
B	BLOOD CREDIT	E	ERROR CORRECTION	H—CO
C	SPLINT CREDIT	F—REBATE	V—TR S
F-249	KEEP THIS BILL. NO OTHER WILL BE ISSUED

SCHEDULE OF RECOMMENDED VISITS & PROCEDURES

Age Months	Procedure	Fee
1	Physical examination, Flouroscopic X-Ray, Measurements, Blood count, conference, diet regulation.	$15.00
2	Physical examination, height & weight, diet regulation.	5.00
3	Physical examination, height, weight, diet. Triple immunizing injection for whooping cough, diphtheria and tetanus (lockjaw).	10.00
4	Same as three months.	10.00
5	Same procedure and injection as at the third & fourth month.	10.00
6	Blood count, physical examination, measurements, diet.	10.00
7	Monthly visit may be eliminated in the healthy infant.	——
8	Physical examination, height, weight, diet.	5.00
9	Monthly visit may be eliminated in the healthy infant.	——
10	Physical examination, measurements and Small Pox vaccination.	8.00
12	Physical examination, weight, measurements, diet, Schick Test for diphtheria immunity.	8.00
15	Physical examination, measurements, diet, Triple booster or re-inforcing injection for diphtheria, whooping cough and tetanus immunization.	10.00
18	Physical examination, measurements, diet, Patch T.B. Test.	8.00
21	Physical examination, measurements, diet.	5.00
24	Physical examination, measurements, diet.	5.00

NOTE: Routine checkups advisable at 2½ and 3 years of age and yearly thereafter. Other procedures as indicated.

The Baby Alumni program began in 1948, giving parents of babies born at Little Company the opportunity to have their child's name and birth date listed in permanent books maintained by the Auxiliary. These special "baby alumni" are remembered in the prayers of the Little Company of Mary Sisters and at special masses offered in the Hospital chapel. More than 50 years later, the books remain on display in the current maternity ward, now the Mother-Baby Unit in the Tower Building and names are still added to the list.

"All of the doctors had to walk through the lobby on the first floor past Mother Dunstan's office. She would see you walking by and call you into her office. She encouraged you to send more patients to Little Company. I practiced at many Hospitals and always felt at home at Little Company. It was a happy place to be and had the feeling of family."

— Dr. Theodore Burkholder

Mother Stanislaus and Mother Dunstan with Dr. Clifford Sullivan, Dr. George Fitzgerald and Dr. Theodore Gasteyer

"For years, many of the physicians at Little Company also took care of workers at South Works, including two renowned doctors, Dr. Chester Zeiss and his brother Dr. Fred Zeiss. Many of us from South Works remember them for their advances in industrial medicine."

— Dr. Frank J. Soltes

Interns

The Junior Service Club

From the pages of the 1947 Junior Service Club Membership Book

DEDICATION

We dedicate this page to

Mrs. Charles Stumpf

Mrs. Arthur Sullivan

Mrs. Chauncey Wilkes

Mrs. Paul Winkler

Mrs. Donald Hogan

Mrs. John Mix

Mrs. Robert Milnes

Mrs. Richard Roche

Mrs. Richard Creevy

Organizers of the Junior Service Club
August 20, 1947

NOTICES

The Junior Service Club of the Little Company of Mary Hospital holds regular Business and Social meetings the First Monday of each month at 8:30 p. m., September to May, inclusive, in the Nurses Home.

Annual Election of Officers is held at the May meeting.

Annual dues are $2.00 payable at the opening meeting in September. New members pay first dues with application for membership.

Members are requested to report to the Courtesy Chairman the birth of a child to a member and the illness or death of a member or in the family of a member.

By September 1948, the needs of the community soon were such that expansion was clearly warranted. Chicago Mayor Martin Kennelly was named honorary chairman of a campaign fund to raise $150,000 to build a five-story addition to the Hospital. In addition to funds raised by the committee, proceeds from the annual football game between the rival squads of Leo and Mount Carmel High Schools held in Soldier Field were generously earmarked for Little Company. By 1949, the final floors were added to the Tower building, which then stood at nine stories.

"After my birth, my mother became very ill and had to stay in the Hospital, so I was kept in the nursery for three weeks, and cared for by my aunt Sister M. Felix. When I was too big for the nursery, I was brought to the Pediatric unit until my mother was well enough to be dismissed from the Hospital – Sisters Felix, de Lourdes and Michael took special care of me."

– Robert M. McIntyre,
Brother of Sister Kathleen McIntye, L.C.M.

1949 – The final floors were added to the Tower Building

"In 1947 I spent the summer at Little Company working in the lab. One of my first jobs was taking notes during autopsies. As an intern, I had a bed near the boiler room."

– Dr. John J. Hurley

Dr. John J. Hurley

June 5, 1947 - Little Company of Mary Hospital's Nurses' Alumni Association, Edgewater Beach Hotel, Chicago

"I was an intern in 1947 and 1948 and played Santa Claus one Christmas Eve. I visited everyone in the Hospital. I became a member of the staff in 1949, and remained there until 1992."

— Dr. Raymond P. Murphy

Hospital Chapel

"I was expecting my first child, Kathy, in November 1946 and I was asked to join the Junior Auxiliary. Little Company was our life then, our social community. The meetings made us feel worldly. Little Company has been an anchor for me. It was a source of joy and a comfort in pain and sorrow."

– Loret Wendt, Auxilian

"In 1947, I was one of three nurse anesthetists at LCM. On my first day, I remember giving anesthesia for 55 patients. That was an extremely busy day. After long days, the Sisters brought platters of sandwiches and goodies into surgery. The LCM Sisters have hearts of gold."

– Mary Lou Zidek, Auxilian

"I joined the staff as an extern from Loyola School of Medicine and was an intern in 1943. Mother Dunstan had a large walk-in safe in her office. She really had no money in it. The Sisters were always gentle, humble and constantly concerned for their patients and personnel."

– Dr. Frank J. Soltes

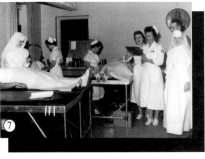

1950s

1 - Surgery, 1950. 2 - Monsignor Thomas Obrycki celebrates Mass. 3 - Pediatrics.
4 - Little Company of Mary Sisters, including two from Evergreen Park, share an audience with Pope Pius XII, June 3, 1953.
5 - Sisters in front of new Convent, 1954. 6 - Physician Dinner. 7 - First blood drive at Little Company, 1957.
8 - Sister Michael Murray, L.C.M., at educational conference, 1957. 9 - Aerial view of Little Company in the 1950s.
10 - Physician team from first organ transplant in the world, 1950. 11 - Convent of St. Joseph with attached Intern Residence.

The Hospital and three members of its professional staff became a part of medical history in June 1950, with the first successful human organ transplant in the United States. The operation, a kidney transplant, was directed by Dr. Richard Lawler, who also was a senior attending surgeon at Cook County Hospital and a member of the faculty of the Stritch School of Medicine of Loyola University. Dr. James West and Dr. Raymond Murphy assisted him in the operation.

The recipient was Ruth Tucker, 49, a Jasper, Indiana, woman who had moved to the South Side with her family to be nearer to medical treatment. She suffered from polycystic kidneys, a condition that had caused the deaths of her mother and sister. At the time of the surgery, her right kidney had only 10 percent of its function remaining and her left kidney was non-functioning.

At 11:30 a.m. on June 17, the operation began with the removal of a healthy kidney from a woman who had died of cirrhosis of the liver. "Not the most ideal patient, but the best we could find," Dr. Lawler said in a later interview.

"We had up to 40 doctors watching. Some of them were even standing on tables in the back," Dr. Lawler said. "A photographer that we had hired to get a motion picture record of the procedure apparently was not accustomed to operations. Midway through, he fainted and one of the doctors in the audience had to take over the camera work."

As the physicians watched, while the movie camera whirred and cameras clicked, Dr. West, who was in the operating room with the donor, handed over the healthy kidney to Dr. Lawler who was attending Mrs. Tucker. Within 45 minutes of the donor's death, the transplant had been completed and blood was flowing through the kidney placed inside Mrs. Tucker.

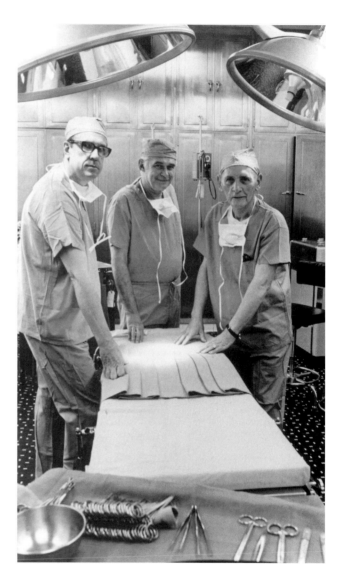

First transplant team included (left to right) Drs. Raymond P. Murphy, James West, Richard Lawler who posed together again in 1972.

Mrs. Tucker walked out of the Hospital the following month, viewed by many as a medical miracle. Her survival astonished both critics and supporters. The surgery had been performed

This dedicated team of physicians performed the first organ transplantation operation in the world at Little Company of Mary Hospital on June 17, 1950. From left: Raymond P. Murphy, M.D., Edward J. Clancy, M.D., Richard Lawler, M.D., James West, M.D. and P.H. McNulty, M.D.

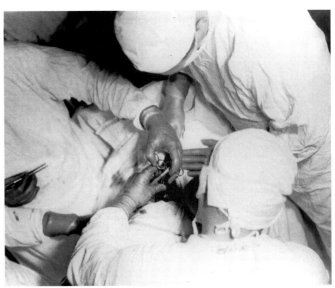

Kidney Transplant

without anti-infection drugs, tissue typing or other advances that would later be taken for granted. Mrs. Tucker's operation was a challenge that inspired pride in the entire medical profession. It would be performed almost routinely within a few decades.

"My father, Dr. Richard Lawler, was a gentle healer, a concerned, caring physician with a vision he dared to pursue—as a courageous pioneer of organ transplantation. I'm proud of his significant contribution to medical science and to the history of Little Company of Mary Hospital, which he so loved," said Christine Lawler Nagle.

Mrs. Tucker lived five years after her surgery, passing away from a coronary occlusion, which followed a bout of pneumonia. Dr. Lawler passed away in 1982, but many of the other people involved in this historic event are still a part of the Little Company of Mary Hospital family. Dr. James West is retired from Little Company. In addition to his

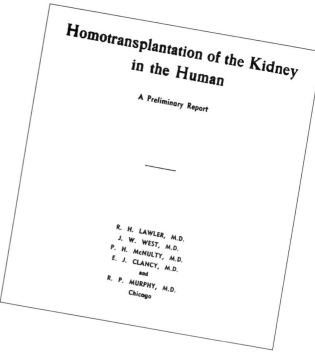

Homotransplantation of the Kidney in the Human

A Preliminary Report

R. H. LAWLER, M.D.
J. W. WEST, M.D.
P. H. McNULTY, M.D.
E. J. CLANCY, M.D.
and
R. P. MURPHY, M.D.
Chicago

November 4, 1950 – Report on Kidney Transplant appears in Journal of the American Medical Association

pioneering efforts in transplantation, he was instrumental in advancing the study of alcoholism as a disease through his work to launch the Betty Ford Clinic and his many years as the Clinic's medical director. He now lives in California.

Dr. Raymond Murphy, also retired and is still an active member of the Evergreen Park community. Sister Joseph Casey, L.C.M., who as a student nurse cared for Mrs. Tucker, has been a Sister of the Little Company of Mary for 50 years and now serves as a Patient Advocate at the Hospital. Mary Lou Zidek, a nurse who assisted the anesthesiologist during the surgery, has been a dedicated volunteer and a member of the Hospital Auxiliary for many years. Nora O'Malley, the scrub nurse, is retired and now lives in McHenry, Illinois.

That same year, in August, ground was broken for a new convent for the Sisters and in June of 1952, Bishop William O'Brien dedicated the Convent of the Maternal Heart.

September 14, 1951 – Convent construction

"One of my most treasured memories is having the privilege of scrubbing in on the first kidney transplant operation in history. This was performed at Little Company of Mary Hospital in the early fifties. The patient was a lovely women from Jasper, Indiana and she, as well as Doctors Lawler and West and the Sisters, were truly courageous pioneers in the advancement of effective health care."

– Nora C. O'Malley, R.N.

The Sisters' Convent

"When my father was on staff at Little Company, I spent many Sundays there. The Sisters always had great chicken dinners on Sundays."

– Dr. John Dwyer, Jr.

Another chapter in the Hospital's rich history began in 1950, when Father Thomas Obrycki, a native South Sider, arrived at Little Company. Months earlier, while vacationing in Colorado with five other priests, their car skidded out of control off a mountain road. While the other priests escaped with minor injuries and cuts and bruises, Father Obrycki suffered a broken neck and was left a quadriplegic.

After more than a year of rehabilitation, Mother Dunstan, hearing of his plight, invited him to make his home at Little Company. "As a guest," she said, "and stay for 100 years – you will bring blessings on us." He was then admitted by Sister Joseph Casey and began living at the Hospital, where he would receive daily medical care and physical therapy. He soon became an inspiration to patients and staff alike, turning a physical tragedy into a personal triumph.

A few years after the accident, Dr. Frank Howard performed surgery on Father Obrycki's hands to help him grasp objects, enabling him to say Mass daily in the sun parlor near his room. He taught boys from nearby parishes how to be altar boys, and one of those boys, young Bill Farrell, grew up to be an orthopedic surgeon. Several years later, the Hospital's maintenance staff made a special altar for Father Tom so that he could offer Mass in the Chapel each morning.

Eventually, Father Tom began the Apostolate of the Handicapped for the Archdiocese of Chicago and was elevated to Monsignor soon after. During the 47 years he resided at Little Company, Monsignor Obrycki gave unselfishly, performing weddings, baptisms and funerals for nurses and friends, assisting in adoptions and inspiring all those who knew him.

"When I came to Little Company in 1965, as a new graduate in physical therapy, one of the first people I met was Father Tom Obrycki. He was brought down to physical therapy each day and bathed in our Hubbard tank. As I exercised his limbs, we became close friends. Father Tom always asked about my family – he baptized our youngest son Jamie – and attended our Physical Therapy Department's Christmas parties every year," said Ray May, Little Company's director of Physical Therapy. "He was a really special man who leaves a legacy as friend, mentor and advocate for the oppressed and needy among us."

Monsignor Obrycki was a common sight at the Hospital's 94th Street entrance, sitting outside in his wheelchair on sunny days with his Panama hat perched on his head, listening to a baseball game and greeting employees and visitors alike, giving advice and blessings as needed. His fellow priests visited Monsignor often, taking him out to dinner and other gatherings. Over the years, Monsignor attended countless Hospital and Auxiliary events, always showing his good humor and ready to offer advice and comfort.

Monsignor Thomas Obrycki with caregivers

"The most touching and rewarding of my nursing student years was my introduction to the late Monsignor Obrycki. Sister M. Helena asked me to stay late and admit him from another Hospital. He arrived at 7:30 p.m. on a stretcher. From that day on we were close friends."

– Sister Joseph Casey, L.C.M.

Silver Jubilee

The year 1955 was a special one for Little Company, as Samuel Cardinal Stritch, Chicago's Mayor Kennelly and more than 1,000 people gathered at the Palmer House Hotel on January 19, to celebrate the Hospital's Silver Jubilee. It was momentous, as Little Company had firmly established itself as one of the leading institutions responsible for making Chicago a world medical center.

Cardinal Stritch praised the Little Company of Mary Sisters for their healing presence in the community. He noted that the Hospital, which had opened during a bleak period of the Depression, had grown in affection as residents in the area came to look upon it as more than a Hospital. The criticism of 20 years earlier,

Cardinal Stritch

when some suggested that locating a Hospital at 95th Street and California Avenue was too far to go for treatment, had long since been stilled—Evergreen Park's population had increased more than tenfold, jumping from 1,600 in 1930 to about 19,000 in 20 years.

The Jubilee was a time to honor the work of key personnel, including six doctors who had been with the staff since the Hospital's opening. Recognized were Dr. Warren W. Furey, Dr. William Malone, Dr. E.D. Huntington, Dr. Anna Robinson, Dr. Roy M. Langdon and Dr. Edmund G. Lawler.

"The Sisters were like family to me. I remember the jokes and songs at the staff dinners in the basement of the Hospital and then later at Beverly Country Club."

— Dr. William B. Sullivan

During this important decade, the Women's Auxiliary came to play a vital role in raising money for the Hospital. The money raised by the Auxiliary in 1952 was used for a "milk laboratory," where formulas were made and bottles were sterilized for the nursery.

Proceeds raised through "High Fever Follies," a talent show held at Fenger High School in 1955, were used to purchase beds for infants and children in the new 100-bed pediatric unit, occupying the entire ninth floor of the Hospital. The Junior Service Club's "Holiday Ball" at South Shore Country Club was another popular and well attended fundraiser.

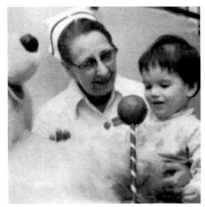

Ms. Viola Luke with pediatric patient

Known for the large number of general practitioners – 60 of the staff of 150 physicians – Little Company of Mary was a general Hospital, but was viewed by many as a maternity center. It was affectionately known as "The Baby Hospital." With about 5,000 births recorded in 1956, Little Company was second only to Cook County Hospital in the number of babies delivered.

"In 1956 through the early 1960s, I recall Sister Rita, Sister Bernadette and Sister Adrian working in Obstetrics. They were working very hard at the time and the Obstetrics Department was very busy. We delivered hundreds of babies a month at the Hospital. The Sisters said that the Holy Spirit was always hovering over the department watching over everyone. It was the busiest time in Obstetrics."

– Dr. Joseph Gallagher

Sterilizing bottles in the milk lab

Junior Service Club
Little Company of Mary Hospital
Evergreen Park, Illinois

The following is a list of the equipment and cash we have donated to the hospital during the six years we have been organized;

Articles donated by Junior Service Club to Hospital up to Nov. '52.

72 Plastic Cribs @ $200	$14,400.00
1 Isolette	730.00
1 Croupette Machine	300.00
1 Bottle Warmer	500.00
Set Venetian Blinds nursery	100.00
3 Air Filter @ $30	90.00
3 Inhalators @ $30	90.00
1 Autoclave	500.00

Articles purchased this year:

2 Iron Lungs @ $1750	$3500.00
2 Isolettes @ $730	1460.00
1 Bottle Warmer	500.00

Annual Cash Donations: to hospital:

1950	$2000.00
1951	7000.00
1952	4000.00
1953	8000.00

Thanking you for your time and consideration and hoping to hear from you at your earliest possible convenience, I am

Yours Very Truly,

Mrs. George Wendt (Public Relations Chairman)
9126 S. Bishop St.
Chicago 20, Ill.
Phone: BE 8- 4182

November 1952 - Report of Junior Service Club donations

"In the 1950s our members from the Christian Reformed Church on 95th Street and Homan Avenue would sing Christmas carols at the Hospital and use an old pump organ. Then the Sisters would take us through the tunnel to the convent for cookies."

— Marilyn Dykstra, Volunteer

A *Chicago Tribune* news article noted: "Men whose children have been born at Little Company of Mary are grateful for the warmth and

Nursery

special attention given to their wives. No matter how late the hour, no one arrived to meet a sleepy admitting clerk in a bank-lobby atmosphere. A cheery Sister rushes down the steps, her blue veil whipping in the wind, to greet the prospective mother. The night policeman frequently is so busy wheeling these new arrivals in and out of the elevators he has to take care of his watchman's work on the run."

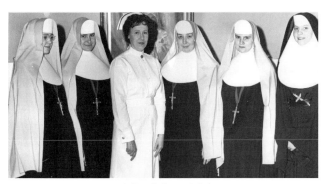
1959 - (left to right)
Sr. M. Bonaventure, Sr. M. Cecilia, Miss Alberta Hilton, Mother M. Magdalen, Sr. M. Lawrence, and from St. Xavier, Sr. M. Bernadette Marie

"In 1950, I became an intern at LCMH and remained an integral part of the Hospital. However, my love of this wonderful institution began much before that. As a youngster I would ride my bicycle to the building and stand and admire it from the outside . . . never

Dr. Delores Lulinski

realizing that some day I would admire it from within.

Some of my fond memories include a visit to the Hospital with our entire wedding party on our wedding day. We had a most pleasant visit with the Sisters; we toasted our marriage with the Sisters and Mayor Kennelly who was visiting Mother Dunstan that day.

The Sisters are a gracious, kind, nurturing and competent group of women. The picture they presented when you entered the Hospital was beautiful beyond words. A Sister, in her white dress and blue veil was seated at the desk in the first floor Rotunda and others were quietly attending patients. As the world changed, the number of Sisters has diminished, but the spirit has been imbedded and will live on as long as Little Company exists.

I am so proud of being part of the medical staff for so many years and for the honor of being the first and only to date, female president of the medical staff."

— Dr. Delores Lulinski

The Hospital became known for its special touches: fathers who sweated out the pre-birth hours in the waiting room often found a tray of hot food delivered to help them through the tense time. An annual Christmas party was held for all of the children born at Little Company. Mothers were taken to what was then uncommon for Hospitals – a recovery ward where they remained for several hours while skilled nurses monitored them for shock and other complications.

The *Chicago Tribune* noted that one day in the nursery, everyone nearby was startled by a piercing whistle. "The alarmed nurses found a new father with two fingers in his mouth, in a taxi calling position, whistling and waving to a tiny bundle on the other side of the glass."

Little Company and the Hospital's administrator Mother Magdalen were the subject of high praise in the media. One newspaper described the facility as "a multimillion dollar establishment, organized by a group of nursing Sisters and operated with spectacular efficiency."

Our beloved Sisters

In acknowledging Mother Magdalen's work, the newspaper described her leadership as "a feat few women in business would care to attempt. The strain of it all, as well as the constant responsibility for hundreds of lives, shows on the quiet face of the administrator – yet her staff probably is as happy a group of dedicated nurses as could be found anywhere."

In June of 1957, a 60-ton frame house at the north end of the Hospital was physically moved – through several blocks of heavy traffic to a new site on the west side of the grounds. It was to be used for a staff recreation room, headquarters for staff and service club meetings and quarters for interns.

Moving Day - Barracks Convent

Annual Picnic

On June 29, 1957, intermittent rain failed to dampen the third annual picnic sponsored by the Little Company of Mary Sisters and held on the north grounds and in the Hospital recreation room. The Sisters prepared food and refreshments while the physicians, nurses, orderlies and other staff members engaged in "games, dancing and frivolity." Among the visitors was Mother Bernard, Superior General of the Little Company of Mary Congregation, who came from Rome to visit the four United States facilities. Contests planned by Sister Mary John Schlax included anatomy tests, suturing contests, tug-of-wars, pie eating, baseball and diaper changing. Races included stretcher bearing, sack and whisk broom sweeping. Members of the games committee included Sister Michael Murray, Mrs. Fred Bartusch, Mrs. Thelma Bienerhaset and Mr. Edward Newmes.

On July 20, 1957, Provincial Mother Mary Genevieve announced members of the Hospital Advisory Board. They included Chicago Mayor Richard J. Daley, Cook County States Attorney Benjamin Adamowski, Chief Cook County

Physicians' Memorial Mass

Municipal Court Judge Raymond P. Drymalski, real estate magnate Arthur Rubloff and a host of other corporate luminaries.

The need for further expansion and remodeling became critical. The number of patients at the Hospital had grown considerably, jumping from 19,452 in 1950 to 25,001 in 1956, an increase of nearly 30 percent. By then the Hospital was operating at 98 percent capacity and had the largest maternity rate of all private hospitals in Illinois. The institution also handled more emergency cases than most hospitals in Cook County, primarily because it was located near industry and main highways.

On October 23, 1957, plans were unveiled to meet the growing medical needs in Chicago's south and southwest areas. A five-floor addition plus six partial floors on California Avenue at 94th Street, as well as extensive remodeling of existing facilities anchored the ambitious plan.

Construction began in the fall, following the launch of an intensive campaign to raise funds from individuals, industry, business, foundations and trade unions. The new addition was to house a

Chapel, major service departments, new patient rooms and a psychiatric unit. The expansion also provided living accommodations for interns and residents as well as emergency and outpatient facilities such as physical medicine, occupational and inhalation therapy departments. At that time, emergency and outpatient facilities increased nearly tenfold—from 1,685 square feet to 14,385 square feet.

"My first visit to the Hospital was on June 28, 1958. I came there to start my rotating internship along with other doctors from Spain, Turkey, Greece, Iran, Mexico and the Philippines. We received so much love and respect from the Sisters, doctors, nurses, nursing students and patients. We felt like it was home. I was a vegetarian and the Sisters took special care of me and sent baskets of fruits to my room. At Christmas there, we had so many gifts we were overwhelmed."

— Dr. P.P. Mangrola

"Around 1950, when I taught in the School of Nursing, Mother Dorothea, who was Superior, was also in charge of the chapel. I taught classes in the late afternoon and on many days, it was my job to help her in the chapel. I always liked that time and duty with her. We seemed close and able to really talk."

— Jean Budding, R.N.

"By expanding and remodeling the existing Hospital plant, we will be able to give the communities we serve a large, modern hospital capable of providing optimum care which is easily accessed by our patients," Mother Genevieve stated.

May 1952
Mother M. Genevieve, Superior

Hospital beds increased from 467 to 550. New and remodeled patient rooms now included modern features such as two-way intercom systems, electrically operated beds, private lavatories, showers and recessed wardrobes. A pneumatic tube system was designed to facilitate rapid transmission of medicines and other materials. And, to the relief of many, air-conditioning was installed in laboratories, outpatient and emergency departments, lounges, administrative offices, the Chapel and many of the patient rooms.

In December 1957, Dr. Warren W. Furey, head of the Hospital's radiology department since the institution opened in 1930, was named head of the medical division of the new development project. Dr. Paul Lawler, who had been chairman of the Obstetrics Department since 1935, assisted Dr. Furey, a past president of the Chicago Medical Society and 1954 recipient of a gold medal from the Radiological Society of North America.

Funds for the challenging renovation and construction program came from a variety of sources, and the efforts ranged from the large to small. Hospital employee Elio Grandi hosted a spaghetti dinner at his home, charging $3 per person. About 40 co-workers accepted the invitation and found Grandi's table covered with bowls containing 15 pounds of spaghetti, 175 meat balls, salad and wine. His Irish wife prepared the dinner with the assistance from Grandi's mother.

In January of 1958, Dr. Francis J. Soltes was

"As a new LCM employee, I was happy to be invited to the annual physicians' dinner. They were giving away a console color television. Dr. Chester Zeiss said that whoever won it should donate $750 to $1,000 to the good Sisters. I could only pray my name would not be called. I also remember with fondness being invited to the convent after Christmas midnight Mass. For many years, it was something I looked forward to."

— Joseph Burger

elected chief of the Hospital's medical staff. A native Chicagoan, Dr. Soltes was a graduate of the Stritch School of Medicine, Loyola University. Mother Mary Genevieve, president of the Hospital board, named Mrs. James Todd to be Hospital Administrator in May of 1958.

The new 400-car parking lot officially opened in June, as Mother Genevieve cut the ribbon for the U-shaped parking area west of the Hospital. The ceremony was attended by Dr. Paul E. Lawler, Dr. Warren Furey, Dr. J.M. Moore, Evergreen Park Mayor Joseph H. Tanner, Susan Kelly, Chief of the Medical Staff Dr. F.J. Moore and other Hospital staff and friends.

"The Sisters played a very positive role in the lives of families on the South Side — many young women trained at Little Company of Mary and became nurses all over the world."

— Margie Meegan Christianson, Class of 1954

More than ever, the Hospital was living up to its reputation as a center for new births. While births were decreasing across the country in the first three months of 1957, the number of babies born at Little Company during that same time was on the rise. Indeed, the number of births in the first three months, a total of 1,517 – about 16 per day – was 13.5 percent higher than the same period in 1956.

*1957 -
Sister Nancy Boyle,
Supervisor with
2-South Head Nurse*

The graduating classes of the nursing and radiology program at the Hospital also continued to increase. In June of 1958, 55 nurses and seven technicians were graduated from the nursing and radiology program of the Hospital at ceremonies held at St. Bernadette's Church. Nursing School Administrator, Sister Mary Carmelita conferred diplomas. The following year, 59 nurses and 13 technicians were graduated.

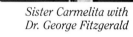

*Sister Carmelita with
Dr. George Fitzgerald*

"Margie and I had average grades and needed to study more. Sister Dorothea called us from the dorm into her office and said, 'Now, girls, you must study.' She gave us a pleasant lecture about our grades instead of being mean about it. Everyone was very fond of Sister Dorothea, she was very kind and sweet to us."

— Mary Lee and Margie Meegan Christianson,
Class of 1954

Sister Carmelita and Sister Benedicta with student nurses

In July of 1958, Mrs. Stanley Ruzich was elected president of the Mother Mary Potter Guild, the Auxiliary of the Hospital. That year the Guild sponsored "All About Love," a situation comedy starring Wendy Barrie and Dennis Morgan at the Drury Lane Theater. Proceeds went to the development program at Little Company. In December of 1959, the Mary Potter Guild held its dinner dance, "Christmas Fantasy," at the Ambassador West Hotel, with about 300 guests in attendance. The table decorations were made by the Guild members, with three-story tiers of crystal goblets sealed together, each holding a Christmas scene in miniature. At the time, the Guild was engaged in a three-year project to raise funds for a cobalt machine for the Hospital's radiation oncology department.

First gift shop opens in main lobby

Joseph Arnold
Chief Pharmacist

"My first job as a high school student was in the Pharmacy, working for Joe Arnold. He was truly a kind man and I loved working at the Hospital. It did help that I knew most of the Sisters, for my aunt was Sister M. Felix."
— Mary Ellen Chambers, Auxilian and
Sister of Sister Kathleen McIntyre, L.C.M.

"The first doctors' dinners were not family affairs as they are today. It was all males in the meeting room. The Sisters would put on aprons and serve the meal. Then the men played cards all night."

— Dr. John J. Hurley

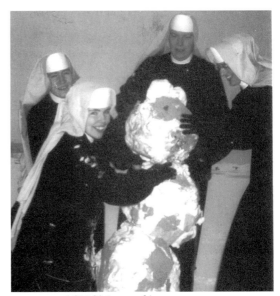

LCM Sisters making a snowman

Little Company's distinctive nurses' cap was redesigned by a student, Marilyn Jordan, who, according to legend, drew it on a paper bag. The cap was first worn at the graduation of the Class of 1953. The four soft pleats in the crown represent faith, hope, charity and prudence. The pleats are held together by a gold bar, which signifies unity. The two side distinctive wings are reminders that actions and thoughts of the wearer are directed toward God. The two buttons in the back represent wisdom and fortitude.

Little Company's distinctive nurse's cap

"I came to work as a nurse's aide for the summer in 1957, and never left. I worked for Sister Gerard (Sister Nancy Boyle) and Sister Christopher. I knew I was home. Over the years, I've worn many hats — nurse's aide, student, R.N., patient (seven children born there), Director of Mission, volunteer and LCM Associate. I'm so grateful to have been a part of the Sisters' journey as they have touched the lives of so many."

— Carol Cassidy Andrews, R.N., Class of 1960

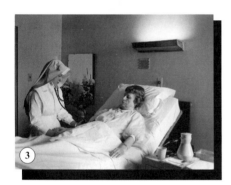

1960s

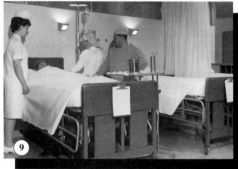

1 - Little Company Physicians' Band. 2 - School of Nursing cap and pin ceremony. 3 - Little Company of Mary Sister ministers to the sick.
4 - Electroencephlograph, 1964. 5 - Archbishop Cody officiates at ceremony when two postulants received habits and five novices professed vows as
Sisters of the Little Company of Mary, 1966. 6 - Clinical education at bedside. 7 - Sister Mary Luke, L.C.M., working in the Lab.
8 - Breaking ground for Education Building, 1967. 9 - Intensive Care. 10 - 1963 School of Nursing graduates.
11. Sister Mary Magdalen, L.C.M., in Orthopedics.

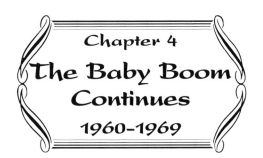

Chapter 4
The Baby Boom Continues
1960-1969

In 1960, the 30th anniversary of Little Company found Hospital officials putting the finishing touches on a comprehensive disaster plan that was singled out for acclaim by the National Safety Council. It was, perhaps, a prophetic time for Hospital officials – their readiness would be tested in the years to come.

The plan, which had been developed over a 12-year period, was so well received that the Safety Council distributed it as a model for other metropolitan hospitals. The plan called for swift handling of large numbers of victims during an emergency. It also provided for use of the Hospital, convent, St. Bernadette School, Northeast Public School, St. Xavier College and Mother McAuley and Brother Rice High Schools in times of emergency.

One particular feature of the plan established units resembling flying squads, which included a doctor, several nurses and nurse's aides. The teams would be dispatched to a disaster area, make preliminary examinations, give first aid and tag the injured at the scene, continue medical aid and route the patient to the proper spot in the Hospital for further treatment.

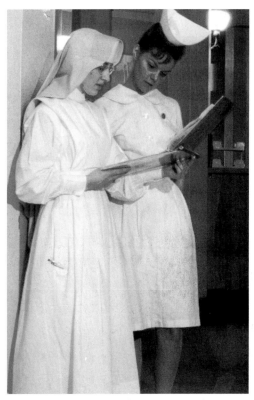

Sister Terrence with a nursing student

The Barrett Family
Sister M. Felix Barrett, L.C.M. and her brothers and sisters - Standing (left to right) Julia Clark, Andrew Barrett, Michael Barrett, Jack Barrett, Thomas Barrett, Dennis Barrett and Sister M. Felix Barrett, L.C.M. Seated (left to right) Nora O'Malley, Mary Greaney and Ellen "Nell" McIntyre

Under the plan, two units would be sent to disaster scenes and four units would serve as admitting teams. Once admitted, patients would be treated by disaster teams within the Hospital in the shock room, burn room, surgical rooms, fracture rooms, minor surgery rooms and medical rooms.

Dr. James West was elected president of the medical staff in January, succeeding Dr. Soltes. Dr. West had been a member of the Hospital surgery staff since 1940. Dr. S.N. Saletta, Dr. W.G. Shurtz and Dr. C.P. Sullivan were honored in February of 1960, with the presentation of certificates for 25 years of meritorious service.

"I joined the medical staff in 1963 as an associate of Dr. William Hagstrom, Sr. Several of my children were born there. One of them, Charlie, came down with a high fever and Dr. Martin Sacks saved his life. In 1972, Dr. Martin McCarthy saved my life with a daring new surgical procedure. Because of overcrowding at the time, I believe I was the first male patient to be bedded in the obstetrics wing."

– Dr. Charles L. Range

1961
Dr. James W. West passes the gavel to Medical Staff President, Dr. Stanley E. Ruzich, as Mother M. Ignatius looks on.

"I remember the kindness of the Sisters who would often come by and offer a kind word of support. In particular, Sister Leo would come by in the late evening with sandwiches for the interns that were working late with patients."

— Dr. Charalambos Stavrakos

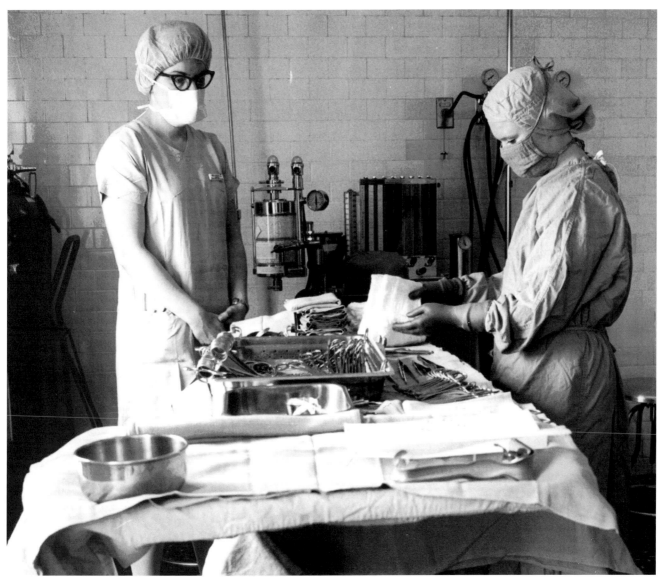

1967 – Student Mary J. Harris sets up surgical instruments in the lab instruction operating room

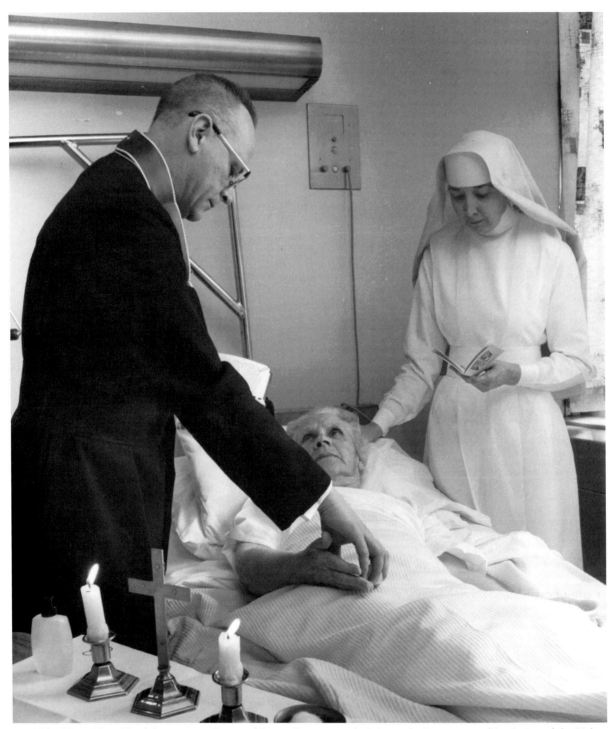

1965 – Sister Mary Magdalen prays as Reverend James Zanmeyer administers the Sacrament of Anointing of the Sick

"I am glad and proud to have been a member of the Little Company of Mary medical staff as a practicing Otolaryngologist since 1960. A few years ago, a young woman and her parents visited me. When she was born, she was unable to breathe through her nose, which I corrected with surgery. She came to thank me and tell me she was engaged to be married."

— Dr. Louis F. Scaramella

The Hospital expansion project was well under way and was completed later that year, bringing the total number of patient beds to 600, quadrupling the institution's capacity since its opening. In June, Cardinal Albert Meyer officiated at the dedication of the new addition.

The Mother Mary Potter Guild played an increasingly significant role in fund raising and providing volunteer services. In June of 1960, the Guild opened its Trading Post Resale Shop at 9118 South Ashland Avenue. The shop sold a wide variety of items, including furniture, jewelry, books and paintings. Sixty-five members of the Guild volunteered a day or more each week.

Auxiliary Trading Post

In August of 1960, the Guild donated a cobalt 60 radioisotope unit to the Hospital. The unit, the first of its kind to be used at a hospital in Illinois, was a significant tool in the treatment of cancer patients.

The Guild followed up with the purchase of two cardioverters, electronic equipment that restored abnormal heart rhythm by electrical counter shock. In later years, the group also purchased mechanical beds, established scholarships for student nurses, donated funds for the Education Building, and remodeled the 2800 Gift Shop and the fathers' waiting room on the maternity ward.

During the 1960s, the Women's Guild underwrote an arts and crafts program for patients. They made rounds to patient rooms with a gift cart, a miniature shop on wheels that carried various sundries for sale to patients for their convenience and comfort. New mothers could also find birth announcements and small toys to bring home to their other children.

Dr. Stanley E. Ruzich was elected president of the

May 1968 - Grand opening of the 2800 Gift Shop
Lois McGoldrick, Sister M. Christopher, L.C.M., the 2800 Gift Shop's first customer and Marion Ruzich

Edna Wooding and Mabel Sorenson in the Gift Shop

medical staff in February of 1961. In March, Hilda Doermann of Blue Island, an eight-year veteran of the Credit and Collection Department, was named "Employee of the Year" and went on to compete in the Chicago Hospital Council's Employee of the Year Contest. Hospital officials praised her excellent work habits, her loyalty to the institution and her genuine concern for the welfare of the patients and patients' families.

During the Hospital's continuing expansion, the obstetrics department was a place of constant motion. So, the incident in the waiting room in June 1961 was perhaps inevitable. Two husbands were pacing the expectant fathers' room when a nurse walked in and asked for "Mr. Delaney." Both men stopped and looked up.

"Mr. James Delaney," the nurse added. Both men moved forward. They exchanged quizzical looks. But the confusion was quickly cleared up. James Delaney, of 17305 Forestway Avenue in East Hazel Crest, a market analyst for Standard Oil Co., shook hands with Chicago police officer James Delaney, of 7810 Cornell Avenue in Chicago. They learned both their wives had given birth that day. Jean Delaney of East Hazel Crest gave birth to a 9-pound, 9-ounce son named Brian. Dolores Delaney of Chicago delivered a 7-pound, 9-ounce daughter, named Maureen Ellen.

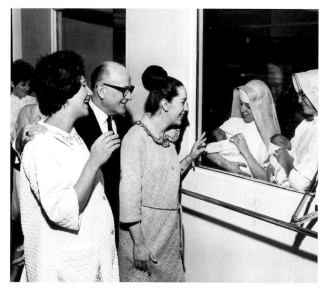

Visit to the nursery

1968 - Sister Joseph Casey with a pediatric patient

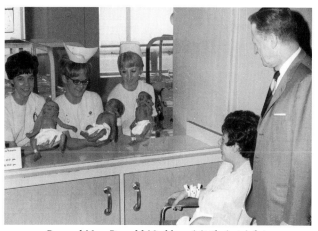

Dr. and Mrs. Donald Madden visit their triplets

The number of births at the Hospital had grown from 230 during the institution's first year in 1930 to more than 5,000 births per year during its peak in the 1950s and '60s.

Intensive Care Unit

"Sister Terrence and Dr. Stavrakos taught the nurses all so much about cardiac care. Often in the evening we would work very late to do a catheterization on a patient or a special procedure and Sister was often the one to make sure that everyone not only laughed, but felt appreciated by the Hospital for their contribution."

— Joan Murphy, R.N., Ph.D.,
Director of Public Relations and Health Promotions

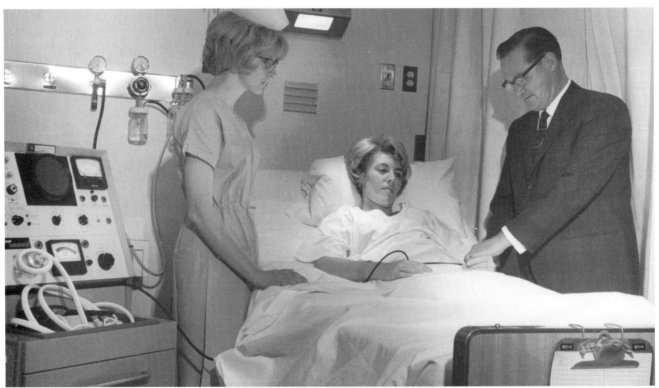

October 31, 1966 – Dr. William B. Knapp visits a patient in M.I.C.U.

"My husband worked at Little Company – and we had our first child there in 1966 – we had a new insurance policy and no coverage for the birth. By today's standards it wasn't much money, but we were very worried about paying our hospital bills. Ray shared our concerns with his boss, Joe Burger. The day our daughter Elizabeth was born, Joe told us that the Sisters said not to worry any more. The Hospital bill was their gift to us! We were overwhelmed by their kindness and will always be grateful for their generous spirit," said Mary Jo May, Executive Director, Little Company of Mary Hospital Foundation.

"During the Baby Boom of the '50s and '60s, Little Company had a 'Cheaper by the Dozen' custom: After having 11 babies at LCM, number 12 was free – a real bonus baby!," said Mary Jo May. "Often, the rooms were all full and moms were lined up in the hallways and solarium waiting for a room. We had our three babies in rather rapid succession in 1966, '68 and '69, and upon leaving for home, I always loved hearing the nurses say 'See you next year' to the moms, who promptly responded, 'Okay.' Baby girls' identification bracelets were blue for the Blessed Mother and the boys wore pink for the Sacred Heart. Sister Bernadette O'Hara and then Sister Rita Bracken provided a wonderful environment in which to have a baby – five days of 'vacation' and meeting new friends. Now Little Company boasts almost 200,000 'baby alumni,' all distinguished, of course."

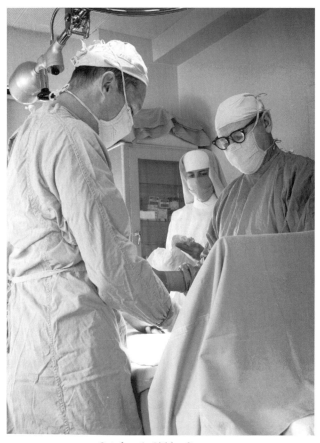

October 1, 1964 – Surgery
(left to right) Robert J. Pike, M.D.,
Sister Mary Louis, L.C.M. and Martin J. McCarthy, M.D.

"Little Company was my home and my ministry, both of which I truly love. During the 1960s we established the Medical, Surgical and Cardiac Intensive Care Units. I remember the dinner that the 10 Sisters served in the convent recreation room. And at Thanksgiving, Hospital administrative staff served our employees – and still does."

– Sister Terrence Landini, L.C.M.

In 1963, the Medical Intensive Care unit opened, one of the first of its kind in the nation. Dr. Leonard P. Brodt was elected president of Little Company's medical staff and in May, Sister Margaret Christina Hoban was named director of the medical records department.

The Surgical Intensive Care unit opened in 1964, and in 1966, the Cardiac Intensive Care unit opened. In 1968, Mayor and Mrs. Richard J. Daley were on hand for the opening of the new School of Nursing Education Building.

"I served my internship under Dr. Fred Zeiss, served my residence at Northwestern University Hospital and then returned to Little Company. It was my home away from home. I had my first operation at Little Company – I broke my ankle as a child. I was fortunate to participate in the growth of orthopedics at the Hospital, which was instrumental in joint replacements at the time."

– Dr. James A.K. Lambur

October 31, 1964 - Honorable Cornelius J. Herrington drives Evergreen Park Mayor Henry Klein onto new parking lot after the dedication ceremony.
(left to right) Smiling with approval are Mother M. Oliver, Mother M. Ignatius, Mother Margaret Mary and Sister M. Christopher.

The Ernest G. Shinner Foundation made a substantial donation for a new addition to the Hospital's School of Nursing in 1964. Shinner, who died in 1963, was a merchant, banker, author and philanthropist with a particular interest in vocational training. The new facility was greatly needed as 102

February, 1967, School of Nursing Education Building ground breaking

qualified students had been turned away in 1962 and 1963 due to lack of space. The one-story building, named the Ernest G. Shinner Memorial Hall, housed science laboratories, classrooms, a large lecture hall, faculty and administrative offices, a lounge and a closed-circuit television system.

In 1968, the new Nursing Education Building officially opened. Mayor Richard J. Daley and his wife, Eleanor, attended. In conjunction with the opening of the School of Nursing Education Building on Saturday, February 24, 1968, *Up With Music,* a musical variety show, was presented with a cast of more than 100 performers. Other groups participating in *Up With Music* were the Doctors' Band, the School of Nursing Glee Club, the Accordiannaires from the Music Center and the Beverly Hilltoppers Barbershop Chorus. Sister Mary Michael was the honorary chairman for the entire program. Actress Charmain Carr, a Chicago girl who began her film career as Leisl in the motion picture version of *The Sound of Music,* flew in from the West Coast to attend the opening of the Education Building and appear in the opening night performance of *Up With Music.* This sold out performance was sponsored by the Mother Mary Potter Guild.

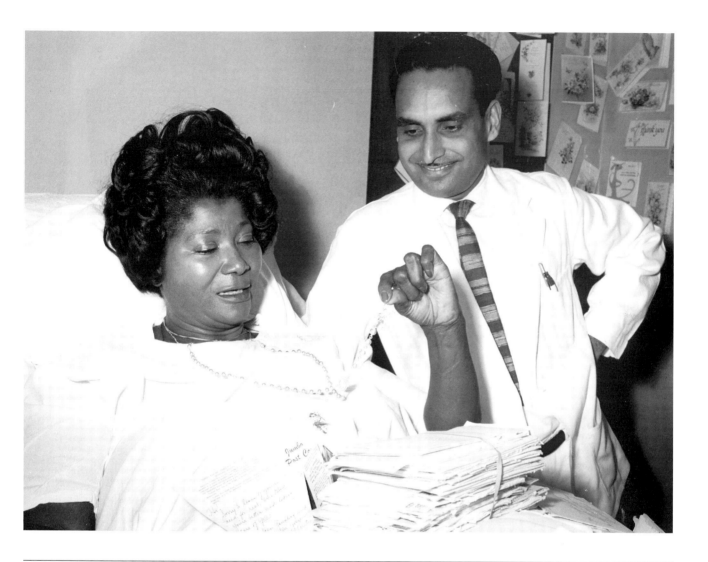

"As house night supervisor, I quickly learned to expect the unexpected. In 1964, I was called at 4 a.m. by the floor's night nurse who was worried about her celebrity patient in room 619. Mahalia Jackson, the renowned gospel singer, has awakened and wants to write a song, she said. The nurse felt she might be confused, but I thought differently. To an artist, the creative moment needed to be captured – and Mahalia, not wanting to lose the moment, asked that someone sing her newly composed lyrics.

As I entered her room, she quickly asked, 'Can you sing?' I said, 'Yes,' but was worried about disturbing the sleeping patients down B-Wing. She then told me she had been invited to sing at Lyndon Johnson's Presidential Inauguration, and was discouraged that her heart condition might not allow her to fly to Washington D.C. Hastily she gave me her newly written lyrics to 'Onward Christian Soldiers'. . . and I began to quietly sing 'Onward President Johnson.' She was like a conductor as she coached me as I sang – I actually thought she might send me to the Inauguration in her place.

Weeks later I received a letter from her reminiscing about our meeting and found a copy of the letter she sent to President Johnson telling him of her stay at LCM and the circumstances in which she wrote the lyrics for the song."

– Peg Schneider, R.N., Chaplain

*August 1, 1964 - Graduation ceremony for the School of Nursing,
the School of Medical Technology and the School of Radiologic Technology in the new Chapel*

In response to a critical need for laboratory personnel, Little Company and Swedish Covenant Hospital on Chicago's North Side established the first federally-sponsored classes for laboratory assistants. Under the direction of Sister Rosarii, 14 women enrolled and learned laboratory procedures in bacteriology, blood banking, chemistry, hematology, parasitology, serology and urinalysis.

By 1966, the Hospital staff had grown to almost 1,300 employees. The prior year had been a typically busy one with 20,720 patient admissions. The obstetrics unit reported 5,059 births and more than 25,000 patients visited the Hospital emergency room.

While the nation was still heavily involved in the Vietnam War, civil defense drills still were carried out to maintain preparedness for nuclear attack. In October 1966, such a drill sent about 110 people into a basement air raid shelter measuring only 100 feet by 35 feet. For 24 hours, participants underwent a mock nuclear attack and subsisted on rationed water and "survival biscuits," a high-calorie cracker that looked and tasted like a graham cracker. Among the patients were 60 Hospital employees who were enrolled in the institution's shelter management program. At the completion of the course, the employees were qualified to direct operations of an air raid shelter.

On January 26, 1967, Chicago was paralyzed during a blizzard called the "storm of the century." Little Company and the surrounding area were buried under 23 inches of snow that fell in just over 24 hours. Road conditions were a nightmare and more than 20,000 abandoned cars littered the streets.

"Employees came to work on cross country skis or in a truck," recalled Joan Murphy. Snow fell at a rate of more than an inch an hour and many second-shift workers could not make it to the Hospital. As a result, many of the first-shift employees stayed overnight. "I remember the incredible teamwork to get things together for our patients, including food service, linen and ongoing treatments," Murphy said.

Everyone pitched in, making sandwiches for staff members and patients, working extended shifts, and taking catnaps on cots in the Hospital meeting rooms. Employees gave out surgical gowns as well as toothbrushes and soap.

The Hospital disaster preparedness plans and employee training for large-scale disasters held Little Company in good stead on April 21, 1967, when the most devastating tornado in Chicago history ripped through Oak Lawn, Evergreen Park and Hometown. It lasted only eight minutes, but cut a swath of destruction that left 32 people dead and hundreds injured. Nearly 900 buildings were damaged.

Eighteen people lost their lives near the intersection of 95th Street and Western Avenue. Many died in their cars; others were killed when buildings collapsed.

As victims poured in, the Hospital itself lost power for an hour. Thankfully, a 250-kilowatt emergency generator engaged, allowing treatment to continue uninterrupted. A total of 201 injured people were brought in during the first two hours after the tornado hit the area, 33 patients were admitted. Ten of those patients were in critical condition and two died. Dr. James A.K. Lambur, who was stationed in surgery at the time the tornado hit, recalled, "The Hospital was like a war zone."

May 1, 1963 – May Crowning

An Award of Merit was presented to
Little Company of Mary Hospital that read:

In appreciation of the splendid emergency services rendered to tornado victims on April 21, 1967 by the Hospital's administrative, medical and nursing staffs and by all of its auxiliary and volunteer personnel.

The dedicated efforts of all concerned in saving lives and alleviating suffering constituted community service of the highest order.

presented by

The Chicago Medical Society

"I remember being a part of the South Side St. Patrick's Day Parade on 79th Street, representing Little Company. The student nurses were dressed in starched whites, caps, gloves and navy wool capes with powder blue linings. We paraded in rows behind our School of Nursing banner. We were a proud bunch — proud to be nurses and proud to be from LCM."

– Carol Cassidy Andrews, R.N.,
Class of 1960

Sister Mary Christopher, Hospital Administrator, said the institution would not bill those treated for the emergency care and subsequent outpatient treatment. She said the Hospital considered this to be Little Company's contribution as a community health center for those who needed emergency care.

On May 5, just two weeks later, Father Leonard Rancilio, Hospital chaplain, offered a special eucharistic service in the Hospital chapel for storm victims and members of their families.

In 1968, Sister Mary Christopher announced a special six-week summer program for grammar school and high school students. Called "New Careers in Rehabilitation," the program was directed by Dr. Joseph Koczur and other Hospital staff members. It was designed to expose teenagers to professional opportunities available in health and rehabilitation fields.

1968 - Opening day of the Ernest G. Shinner Memorial Hall Mayor Richard J. Daley with John Burns, Gene Gallagher, Fran Gallagher and John Hyland

"In the 1960s, there was an LCM Sister in charge of every department. You had the opportunity to really get to know them and see how much they devoted their lives to the sick and dying. After Vatican II, many of the Sisters changed from the full habit and veil to the dark suits. Employees had pools as to what style and color hair the Sisters had when they converted to the new veil."

— Ron Skarzynski

"Dr. Ralph Spaeth was our pediatrician for our four children. He treated with love and a minimum of medicines to help the body heal itself. One day, while riding his bicycle through the neighborhood, he made an impromptu stop at our house to check on our children. We marveled at his dedication and long hours."

— Ronald and Jane Drynan

Dr. Ralph Spaeth

"I worked in housekeeping in the summer of 1966, washing walls at the School of Nursing dormitory. I became an attending physician on staff in 1987 and now work in the Hospice Program and with the Alzheimer's patients."

— Dr. Michael F. Thomas

The Auxiliary's seventh annual Garnet Ball was held at the Ambassador West Hotel in January of 1967.
(back) James McGetrick, Mr. Roche, Mrs. Napleton, Betty Napleton, Mrs. Murphy, Mr. Murphy
(front) Pat McGetrick, Mr. Napleton, Mrs. Roche, Russell Streff, Eileen Streff, Francis Napleton

"I started my first job in collection in the business office, then took over data processing, then became a vice president and later became Chief Operating Officer of the Hospital. The love and dedication of the Sisters was built on their humility because of their work in patient care. I accepted their mission as my mission and I was welcomed into a community of loving, caring and sharing. No way could I begin to repay the Sisters for the love I felt from them."

– Ken Hansen

"I grew up in the Intensive Care Unit and it was an exciting time in medical history. We opened the ICUs and developed the code team to respond to cardiac emergencies of patients in the Hospital."

– Dr. Charalambos Stavrakos

1970s

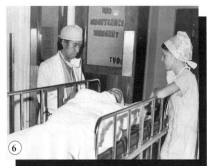

1 - Doctors' lounge. 2 - Little Company of Mary Auxiliary - Sister Mildred, L.C.M., Loret Wendt and Carol Andrews.
3 - Dr. Sachs and resident on Pediatrics Rounds. 4 - Candy Stripers - our first youth volunteers. 5 - Orthopedic Teaching Rounds.
6 - Waiting for surgery. 7 - Dr. C. Stravakos demonstrating equipment in Cardiac Intensive Care. 8 - Celebrating 100 years of caring.
9 - Sister Leo, L.C.M., and Sister Carmelita, L.C.M., review the 1970s Patient Handbook. 010 - Dr. Thomas Gorman delivered Little Company's
145,000th baby to Thomas and Mary Owens. 11 - Jack Faber in Little Company's Pharmacy in the 1970s.

Chapter 5
Expansion Continues
1970-1979

"I have many happy memories of Little Company, but I enjoyed most of my days working as a phlebotomist in the laboratory part-time on weekends in the summer from 1972-77. I had the opportunity to witness health care first-hand and to see many great doctors, nurses and technicians. Little Company was and always will be a warm and compassionate institution."

— William J. Farrell, Jr., M.D.

In January of 1970, Little Company celebrated its 40th anniversary with a week of activities. It began with an open house featuring arts and crafts made by employees and a dinner celebration in their honor presented by the Sisters of the Little Company of Mary. Tuesday was Mother Mary Potter Guild Day with employees and Guild members attending the official opening of the new Father's Waiting Room in the maternity ward. A special anniversary sale was held in the Gift Shop.

On Wednesday of that week, the medical staff was honored with a solemn Mass followed by a brunch. Thursday was Community News Media Day and featured appearances by prominent citizens, community leaders, local and state legislators, the news media and various civic leaders. A special luncheon was followed by a historical review of the Hospital and community. Finally, Friday was set aside to honor nurses and technical personnel. Nurses wore vintage nursing uniforms, and each patient received a commemorative favor. A one-hour program entitled "A Night to Remember," a review of four decades of the Hospital, was presented by nurses.

January 28, 1970 – Physicians' Awards Dinner Walter J. Miller, D.D.S., Msgr. Thomas Obrycki and Sister M. Angela

Nurses wearing historical uniforms (left to right) Diane Chomka, Margaret Littleton, Mary Christian, Mary Alice Sessler and Ethel Misuraca

A Time To Remember . . .
40th Anniversary

January 22, 1970 – 40th Anniversary Celebration, Evergreen Park Mayor Anthony Vacco, speaker

40th Anniversary - Medical Staff Luncheon
Dr. John B. O'Donoghue, Jr., surgery; Dr. Louis F. Scaramella, otolaryngology;
Rev. Richard Rogers, pastor of Trinity Presbyterian Church of Oak Lawn; and Dr. Frank C. Lawler, obstetrics and gynecology

A Time To Remember . . .

Physicians' Awards Dinner – (Seated) Lorrie Craven, Gloria Farrell, Pat Hasbrouck, Loret Wendt, Mary Brophy
(Standing) Dr. Stanley Ruzich, Marion Ruzich, Dr. Bill Farrell, Dr. and Mrs. William Sullivan
Dr. Robert Meaney, Dr. Edward Brophy, Dr. Robert Craven and Dr. Cecil Hasbrouck

"I remember the golf outings that Little Company held at Beverly Country Club when Mary Brophy would sing and entertain us after dinner. She entertained us with her songs. We loved to hear her sing! Those were the days. What fun we all had!"

— Patricia Skarzynski, Volunteer

October 1971 – Sheraton Hotel in Chicago

Plans were in the works to update the x-ray and laboratory departments and the nurses' call system. One hundred fifty small, two-bed rooms were to be converted to large single rooms. The Hospital was greatly overcrowded. Patients were housed in hallways and lounge areas and another 300 people were on a waiting list. Emergency cases were still being accepted, although on some days the unit was filled to capacity.

Dr. William O'Reilly and a patient

"I joined the Hospital medical staff in 1977, and even though there were more than 500 beds at Little Company, the Hospital was always full. Times have really changed in the years since. Patients only stay a few days and now often go home the same day after surgery."

— Kent F.W. Armbruster, M.D.,
Executive Vice President/Medical Director

Soon the Hospital was up to 600 beds with a staff that included 200 physicians and 1,700 employees. In the 40 years since Little Company opened its doors, the institution had grown to five times its original size to become the largest Catholic hospital in the Chicago suburban area. Some 24,000 patients and newborns were cared for annually in addition to more than 36,000 emergency patients.

"My husband, Dr. Clarence O'Reilly, was a surgical resident after his discharge from the Army. It was not only an excellent Hospital, but had especially strong Catholic principles. All of our six children were born there — the first in 1950 and the last in 1970. While my husband was on staff we really had more opportunities to know the Sisters. He was on the Hospital Board of Directors and my son, Bill, followed on the Board many years later."

— Gerry O'Reilly

"My first assignment was Supervisor of the Medical and Surgical Departments at the Hospital. Later I was asked to volunteer in Buenas Aires. After returning I was assigned to the Laboratory. I taught student nurses Microbiology for five years and took pride in that none of them failed exams or the State Board exam."

— Sister Mary Teresa Oleniczak, L.C.M.

May 27, 1970
Jack Faber - Pharmacy

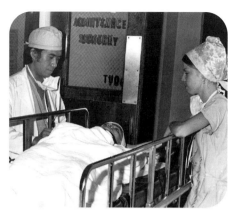

Patient waiting for surgery

Medical Staff Library

October 1971 – Dr. Delores Lulinski, first and only female
President of the Medical Staff

Candy Stripers

January 1970 – Physicians' Awards Dinner
Dr. William Farrell and Walter J. Miller, D.D.S.

January 1970 – Physicians' Awards Dinner
Dr. Edward J. Brophy

In January of the same year, a pediatric cardiology center was opened and operated under advisement of the staff, faculty and personnel of the University of Chicago Hospital complex. Dr. Martin O. Sacks, pediatric director at Little Company and supervisor of the new program, said that pooling staff and equipment provide a higher quality of service for patients. Little Company supplied the space and laboratory work and the University of Chicago supplied the equipment as well as its expertise. Dr. Sacks hailed the unit as a demonstration of the kind of collaboration needed between universities and hospitals.

Dr. Martin Sacks

"During the past two years, adult and child cardiology has become much more sharply separated," Dr. Sacks declared. "Almost all child heart problems are congenital defects while the adult problem is acquired by a heart that was once normal."

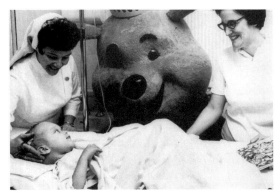

Sister Joseph Casey introduces a visitor to a pediatric patient

Dr. Irene Kuras, Pediatrician

"I was the last family practitioner to deliver babies at Little Company. In one family, I delivered six children. Dr. Theodore Gasteyer delivered half of the generation in Oak Lawn with his wife, who was a nurse."

— Dr. John J. Hurley

"There was a three-year-old boy in Pediatrics with pneumonia. He kept calling for a nurse. After several trips down the hall with water and juice, the night nurse told him to get to sleep so he would get better. By the time she got back to her desk, she could hear him calling, 'Nurse! Nurse!' She went to the intercom and sternly said, 'Go to sleep, NOW!' After a moment of silence, the little boy replied, 'Yes, wall.' He never made another sound."

— Sister Joseph Casey, L.C.M.

*Physicians' Awards Dinner (left to right) Dr. C.J. O'Reilly, Dr. Martin Sacks,
Dr. Raymond P. Murphy, Dr. Arthur Janeke, Dr. Mark Guinan, Dr. Charles Corcoran,
Dr. George Blough, Dr. Kenneth Fitzgerald, Dr. Daniel Oliveri and Dr. John Green*

A Time

To Remember . . .

*Golf Outing Dinner (left to right)
Morgan Murphy, Sr., Congressman Morgan Murphy,
Mrs. Judy Hynes and Cook County Assessor Thomas Hynes*

*Dr. James A.K. Lambur, Dr. S. Javed Shirazi,
Dr. Albert V. Bosch, and Dr. Benjamin A. Jagodzinski*

In January of 1971, Little Company boasted the second birth of the New Year – Shannon McGuire born 10 seconds after midnight. The seven-pound girl was born to Mr. and Mrs. James McGuire.

Later that year, Massachusetts Senator Ted Kennedy attended the opening of Little Company's Neonatal Intensive Care Unit.

Also that year, a new convent for the Sisters opened. The previous convent, adjacent to the Hospital, was converted to offices and treatment areas, relieving crowded conditions in the main Hospital buildings.

The Women's Auxiliary purchased a new linear accelerator in July of 1976 for the radiation oncology department, providing the Hospital with one of the most sophisticated and powerful tools for the treatment of cancer.

Senator Ted Kennedy visits the Sisters.

January 21, 1970 – Father Smolar, C.P.P.S., head chaplain; Reverend Joseph Sheeran, C.P.P.S., chaplain at St. Bernard's Hospital; Dr. Jose M. Cava, division of obstetrics and gynecolog; Rev. Joseph Marciulion, St. Christine's Church; Rev. John Kalicky, C.P.P.S., St. John's Church of Whiting, Indiana, and Sister M. Imelda, emergency room supervisor

Mrs. William Murphy, Mrs. Otto Scheiner, Mrs. Dino Maurizi,
Mrs. Thomas Evans, Mrs. David Beran, Mrs. Louis Scaramella,
Mrs. Francis Napleton, Mrs. Norman Lindh, Mrs. John Hyland,
Mrs. Frank Schaffer and Mrs. Robert Dolehide

John J. Duffy, Barbara Duffy, Mrs. Eleanor Daley,
Mayor Richard J. Daley and Eileen Streff

A Time To Remember . . . Garnet Ball

"I joined the Auxiliary in 1972, just after the first Reflections
fashion show. I was blessed to meet the most wonderful women . . .
so many mentors and friends. Eileen Streff was the Auxiliary
President then, and she was a great role model. As a young volunteer, I learned so much from all the women I met at Little
Company, and I treasure their wisdom and generosity."

— Mary Jo May, Executive Director,
The Little Company of Mary Hospital Foundation

Clockwise from the front: Ray and Mary Jo May,
Joe and Margaret Burger, Fran and Colleen Gallagher, Gene
and Mary Reardon, Al and Maureen Stone and
Ches and Carol Andrews

Mr. and Mrs. Russell Streff

The Sisters' ministry to care for the sick and the dying came full circle when Hospice Care began at Little Company in 1979, just four years after the first hospice program was initiated in the United States. As in the early days after the pioneering Sisters first came to America, nurses and volunteers went to patient's homes, to care for the patients and their families. Hospice care provides emotional support for family members whose loved ones are in the final stages of life. Each patient with limited life expectancy is cared for with dignity and respect by a team of nurses, social workers, home health aides, pastoral care ministers and volunteers, helping them to live life to the fullest, as long as possible, at home and close to loved ones. The program has provided the physical and emotional care that has made a difference to entire families. The program continues to focus on the patient's comfort and provides symptom management, pain control and support.

"In 1973, my father was injured on the job and was pronounced dead in the LCM emergency room. Father Cummings anointed my father, whose last words were, 'May God forgive me.' What a comforting memory of my father and the Chaplain."

— Mary Baldwin Waitches

"In 1977, I decided to take some time off from college to decide what field of endeavor I would like to pursue. A friend of the family, Betty Corcoran, R.N., made me aware of a job opening in the Emergency Room at Little Company of Mary Hospital. This job required prior medical experience, which I did not have. I met with Sister Carmelita Hoban, and she was kind enough to hire me, despite my inexperience. My 'temporary' respite from college lasted 1½ years, during which time I became interested in the field of medicine. I then returned to college and, subsequently, medical school while continuing to work part-time in the Emergency Room. It is because of Sister Carmelita's willingness to give an inexperienced college student an opportunity in the Emergency Department that allowed me to discover medicine and make a career choice that has been very fulfilling."

— Daniel A. Rowan, D.O., Director, Cardiac Catheterization Laboratory

1975 – Dr. Thomas Gorman, Mr. and Mrs. Thomas Owens and
Katie Owens – 145,000th baby born at LCM

"The years I worked in the Cardiac Intensive and the Medical Intensive Care Units, from 1965 to 1975, bring so many touching memories to mind. The Sisters were often present at the death of a patient and it brought so much comfort to the families and the staff caring for the patients. It was most difficult for the staff to see a young man or woman die when they seemed to have so much living yet to do. Somehow the Sisters helped all of us, the nurses and doctors, cope with the end of life as the final step in the journey."

– Joan Murphy, R.N., Ph.D.,
Director of Public Relations and Health Promotions

A Time to Remember . . .

"Dr. Charlie Krause played the trumpet in the Doctor's Band. He was on the staff at Christ Hospital and Head of the Obstetrics Department. We wanted him to play the trumpet in the band so we got him on the staff at Little Company so that he could play in the band."

– Dr. Joseph Gallagher

1977 – Doctor's Band
Dr. Edward L. Jansen, Dr. Robert Gasior,
Dr. Gregory Hernandez, Dr. Joseph T. Gallagher
and Dr. James W. West

Members of the Doctor's Band who furnished
entertainment for their colleagues: (left to right)
Dr. Joseph T. Gallagher, saxophone; Dr. Gregory Hernandez,
bass violin; Dr. Cecil Hasbrouck, drums;
Dr. Ralph Hubble, trumpet; Dr. James W. West and
Dr. James T. Houlihan, banjo; and the pianist beyond camera
range was Dr. Edward L. Jansen

Little Company's Extended Family and Celebrities

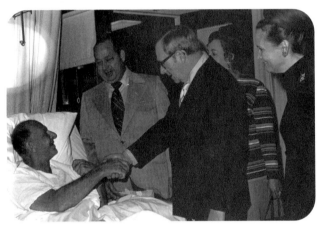

Governor Richard Ogilvie and Mayor Anthony Vacco of Evergreen Park visit a patient.

Wilbur Wood, Chicago White Sox pitcher, visits with a pediatric patient.

Governor Richard Ogilvie visits the Hospital with Sister Joseph Casey, Dr. Ralph Spaeth and John Mortimer.

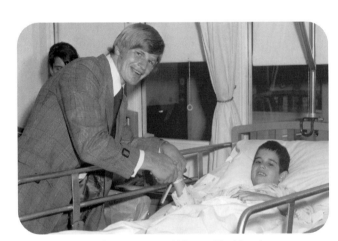

Keith Magnuson, Chicago Blackhawk, visits with a pediatric patient.

Little Company's Extended Family and Celebrities

VIP Tours of the Hospital
Sister Margaret Christina Hoban, L.C.M.,
Dr. C.J. O'Reilly, Paul R. Wozniak and
Governor Richard Ogilvie

Barbara Rooney, R.N., Actress Elke Sommer,
Mary Jane O'Sullivan, R.N. and Dorothy Schaffer, R.N.

Bobby Hull, Chicago Blackhawk,
and Joey O'Shea, pediatric patient

Little Company's Extended Family and Celebrities

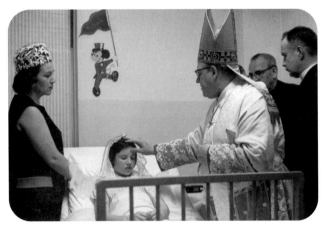

John Cardinal Cody and Mary Rita Raleigh

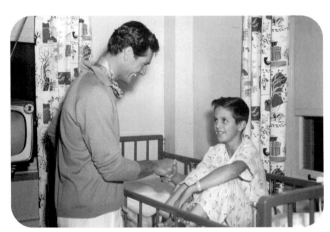

Actor Hugh O'Brien with a pediatric patient

*April 1979 - Auxiliary Officers
Joan Claussen, Mary Lou Langdon,
Mary Jane McDonough, Lillian Meck and Mary Jo May*

*Chicago White Sox owner Bill Veeck,
Sister Nancy Boyle, L.C.M. and Dr. Frank Soltes*

Little Company's Extended Family and Celebrities

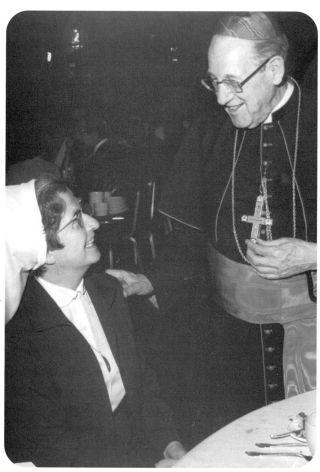

Sister Michael Fitzgibbons, L.C.M. and John Cardinal Cody

ABC-TV Reporter Jim Gibbons interviews the Sisters:
(front) Sister Benedicta, Sister Helen, Sister Agnes,
Sister Joseph Casey, (middle) Sister Jerome, Sister Bernadette,
Sister Regina, Sister Virginia, (back) Sister Mary Babcock,
Sister Mary Jane Feil and Sister Mildred

Sister Joseph Casey, L.C.M.,
Ronald McDonald
and pediatric patients

A Time To Remember . . .

February 22, 1979 – Physicians honored at the Physicians' Awards Dinner
(left to right) Earl A. Vondrasek, M.D., William B. Knapp, M.D., Frank J. Doyle, M.D.,
Joseph L. Koczur, M.D., John F. O'Brien, M.D., John J. McLaughlin, M.D. and Robert P. Meany, M.D.

"The Hospital is noted for clinical education and training of nurses, physicians, physical therapists and numerous other health professions. I joined the Hospital in 1975 as an administrative resident. LCM was a coveted training program for a budding Hospital administrator. St. Louis University and Washington University sent their graduate students to the Hospital for training. During the many months of training, I rotated through 39 different departments and learned about each of the 200 occupations. I marvel today, after 25 years, how the employees as busy as they were, could take the time to train others. I am forever grateful."

— Dennis Day, Vice President, Support Services

Paul Wozniak and Sister Benedicta Mahoney, L.C.M.

July 4, 1977 – Evergreen Park parade float

1 - **South Pavilion.** 2 - **Celebrating 50 years of caring.** 3 - **Oak Lawn Care Station.** 4 - **Sisters attend 1982 Service Awards.**
5 - **The first baby born at Little Company returns 50 years later.** 6 - **Dr. Rafael Vargas visits with young patient.**
7 - **Volunteers have been strong supporters of Little Company.**
8 - **Sister Mary Babcock, L.C.M., Maureen O'Ryan and Grace Wen offer diabetic instruction.**
9 - **Sister Joseph Casey, L.C.M., carries our mission to the community.**
10 - **Paul Wozniak, Dr. Thomas Patricoski and Sister Mildred, L.C.M., at Physicians Dinner.** 11 - **Burbank Care Station.**

*1980s – Physicians honored - (top row) Dr. William Graber, Sr.,
Dr. John Uhrich, Dr. Robert Dolehide (bottom row) Dr. Gene Diamond,
Dr. James Graham, Dr. Joseph Buckley and Dr. Thomas S. Patricoski*

In 1980, Little Company of Mary Hospital celebrated its Golden Anniversary. In celebration of this gala event, the Hospital invited Evergreen Park friends and neighbors to share in the festivities on Saturday, January 19, 1980.

The day began with John Cardinal Cody presiding over a concelebrated Mass at St. Bernadette Church. A dinner-dance followed in the Martinique's Grand Ballroom. Three physicians who had been on the staff since 1930 – Drs. Roy P. Langdon, Ralph E. Jones and Leo P. Sweeney – attended the dinner. Also in attendance was Douglas Kier of Kirkwood, Missouri. Born on January 24, 1930, Mr. Kier was the first of the 155,000 of babies born at Little Company of Mary.

"I started as a nurse extern, working midnights on the sixth floor in 1980. I have fond memories of Dr. John Baron, Dr. Bill O'Reilly and Dr. S. Javed Shirazi. Little Company has been a major influence in both my spiritual and professional life. I joined the Catholic faith 10 years ago and have always felt the Sisters were catalysts for me. Their friendship and support have made my life very full!"

*– Mary Jo Quick, R.N.,
Director of Mission and Values Integration*

Physicians Honored . . .
50 Years on Staff

Dr. Ralph E. Jones

Dr. Roy M. Langdon

Dr. Leo P. A. Sweeney

*Sister M. Terrence Landini, L.C.M. with Dr. Leo P.A. Sweeney,
Dr. Ralph E. Jones and Dr. Roy M. Langdon*

1986 – Physicians' Awards Dinner
Standing: Dr. Jose Cava, Dr. William Sullivan, Dr. Mary O'Neill, Dr. Christopher A. Lekas, Dr. Ralph Spaeth,
Dr. Lydia Kurylak, Dr. Paul Schmidt, Sister Kathleen McIntyre, L.C.M. and Dr. Thomas Gorman
Seated: Sister Francis Thompson, L.C.M., Dr. Edward Jansen and Dr. Donald Madden

1980s – Douglas Kier, first baby born at
Little Company of Mary Hospital and Paul Wozniak

"When I came to LCM 35 years ago, I thought I would be a staff pharmacist here for a few years and then move on. Little did I realize the opportunities for growth and improvement that LCM would offer me. At LCM, people are encouraged to use their talents to the fullest and expand their knowledge beyond their original areas of expertise. The Sisters of Little Company and the other members of the LCM organization continue to look for new ways to bring caring, professional, quality health care to the public, and I am grateful for having contributed to that effort."

– Jack Faber, Vice President Clinical Services
and Corporate Compliance Officer

By that time, Little Company of Mary Hospital had become one of the largest Catholic hospitals in the metropolitan Chicago area. More than 250 physicians were on the medical staff and employees totaled more than 1,900, making Little Company the largest employer in Evergreen Park. The annual patient admissions tally had risen to more than 21,000 and another 42,500 patients were treated annually in the emergency department.

In keeping with Little Company's commitment to family-centered care, Little Company opened its first birthing room, offering expectant parents a comfortable home-like atmosphere as an alternative to the traditional surroundings of labor and delivery. Joseph Edward Merrion, son of Frances and Edwin Merrion, was delivered by Dr. Roy Langdon. They were the first to use the newly designed birthing room.

Education Building T.V. Studio

"Little Company of Mary Hospital has been a part of my life for almost my entire 44 years. I was born there on Father's Day, and later I vividly remember waiting in the playroom for my Father as he finished his patient rounds. While in high school, I had a summer job under the guidance of Ken Buttron in the Grounds Department. In addition, I was a transportation aide in the Radiology Department during college summers. Things turned full circle in 1986, when I returned as an attending physician. Many of the nurses who handed me toys as a child now aided me with patients. Little Company of Mary has been, is now, and always will be a special part of my life. Thank you, Sisters of the Little Company of Mary."

— Brian P. Farrell, M.D.

October 10, 1980 - Birthing Room
Kathi Kavanaugh, Frances and Edwin Merrion,
and Baby Joseph Edward

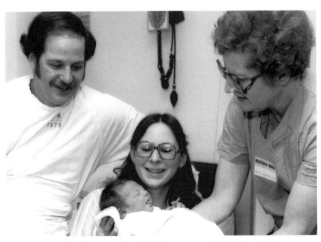
First baby born in 1980, January 4, (left to right)
Robert and Carol Uidl, Zachary Uidl and Mary Alice Davis, R.N.

"I came to LCM in 1968 and worked in the kitchen washing pots and pans part-time while I attended school. That was 32 years ago. I began working full-time at the Hospital in 1971."

— Dennis Reilly, Vice President, Chief Operations Officer

Since the Hospital first opened its doors, Little Company of Mary has had a close relationship with the City of Chicago, as countless numbers of police officers and personnel have been treated. One day in 1982, while the daily pursuit of caring for the sick and injured went on without publicity, the media descended on Little Company when two police officers were brought to the Hospital emergency room with gunshot wounds. As Police Superintendent Richard Brezchek huddled with command personnel and investigators at the Hospital, one of the two officers died of his wounds.

Construction of South Pavilion

The School of Nursing closed its doors in 1984, after 54 years of educating nurses. Four-year baccalaureate programs were gradually replacing two-year diploma programs like Little Company's.

"As I remember opening the first Home Care office in 1984 in the space that everyone referred to as the 'Gift Shop,' I recall thinking this was such a 'gift' that Little Company administration was being so proactive in responding to the change in health care needs by beginning our own Private Duty and Medicare Home Care. Little Company Hospice was already in place and Home Care would complete the 'package' for this forward-thinking Catholic South Side Hospital. This was the philosophy of care provided by the Little Company Sisters to those in need in their own home environment early in the 1920s."

— Peg Radakovitz, Director Adult Day Care and Home Health Equipment Center

Also that year, Little Company celebrated the opening of its new South Pavilion, complete with a new Emergency Room, additional patient rooms, and a new Radiation Oncology Department outfitted with the most modern technology available to treat cancer.

Home Based Services, which began at this time, continued the Sisters' legacy, and brought additional resources to the senior community, once again recalling the Sisters' early mission of caring for patients in their homes. Offering specialized teams of nurses, therapists, social workers, home health aides, pastoral care ministers and volunteers who care for patients in their homes, Home Based Services bridges the gap between home and hospital for as long as help is needed.

South Pavilion

Although the baby boom had long since passed, Evergreen Park Mayor Anthony Vacco noted in 1987, that in the 57 years since Little Company opened its doors, the Evergreen Park Village Hall had become the repository for more than 176,000 birth certificates.

That same year, in one of the first joint ventures of its kind, Little Company collaborated with Palos Community Hospital and St. Francis Hospital and Health Care Center to open the Southwest Hospitals' MRI Center in Oak Lawn, offering the newest technology for magnetic resonance imaging.

Robert Kennedy and Alfred J. O'Malley presenting a donation for the South Pavilion expansion to Sister Terrence Landini, L.C.M.

"I recall in 1984 working with a Hospital team to computerize the physicians' offices, linking them up to the Hospital. We developed a wonderful relationship with physicians' office staff. They came together once a month for breakfast meetings to discuss admitting procedures and how they could help one another, and periodically we would arrange for guest speakers from various Hospital departments to help keep them informed. Ken Hansen was instrumental in making the right choices for computer technology in the 1960s and 70s."

— Dennis Reilly, Vice President, Chief Operating Officer

"Late 1987 and 1988 was a very stressful and busy time for myself. My friend and partner, Dr. Ralph Zitnik, unexpectedly died in mid-1987. An agreement with Northwestern Memorial Hospital was in the process of being arranged to allow cardiac catheterization procedures to be performed at Little Company of Mary Hospital. The brand new Cardiac Catheterization Laboratory opened in July of 1987. At the same time, there was a new administration at Little Company of Mary Hospital. My wife was expecting twins at this time, and had a very complicated pregnancy. She was in the hospital for long periods of time in early 1988. The support and phone calls from Sister Kathleen, Sister Margaret Christina and the other good Sisters were of great personal benefit to me during these very stressful times. I truly felt that I was part of the Little Company of Mary Hospital family. The personal interest that the Sisters took in my life, as well as the lives of my wife and twins, will always be fondly remembered. I continue to be grateful for their friendship and support."

— Thomas J. Quinn, M.D.

Recognizing that services for memory-impaired adults and their caregivers were increasingly needed in the Hospital's service area, an adult day care center for the elderly was opened on the Hospital campus. The Adult Day Care Center provided respite for caregivers and a safe haven for participants, providing socialization, stimulation and friendship for all who spent time there.

Also at this time, Little Company opened its Sleep Disorders Unit to help patients suffering from sleep apnea, insomnia and other sleep disorders in the comfort of a bedroom environment. "With the opening of the Little Company of Mary Hospital Sleep Disorder Center in 1988, the range of services available at the Hospital was expanded into a new arena: the evaluation and treatment of problems specifically related to the one-fourth to one-third of our lifetimes spent sleeping or trying to sleep," said Evan McLeod, M.D., Medical Director, Respiratory Care Department.

"As a child, I often made rounds on Sunday morning with my dad, Dr. William Farrell, a Little Company pediatrician. I would go to the playroom on the pediatric floor, and then we would go to Mass and breakfast in the Hospital cafeteria. Anytime the doctors' kids visited, we wanted to flip the switch on the switchboard at the doctors' entrance. I was born at Little Company and met my wife Colleen there during Medical School. I will always remember how good the Sisters were to our family, especially in 1967, when my sister recovered here after being hit by a car."

— Richard Farrell, M.D.

"My fondest memories are of the many Joint Board retreats my husband, Dr. Bill Farrell, and I attended with the Sisters. Bill was an integral part of the Little Company of Mary mission as he served as the Medical Director. Our sons, Doctors Bill, Brian and Richard have proudly followed in his footsteps, caring for others in the medical field."

— Gloria Farrell

Remembering the . . .
1980s

1983 – Annual brunch for major benefactors
Francis Gallagher, Sister Mildred Radziewicz, L.C.M.,
Cardinal Joseph Bernardin, Rose Lamb,
Sister M. Magdalen, L.C.M., Matt Lamb,
Sister Margaret Christina Hoban, L.C.M. and Robert Watkins

Sister Margaret Christina Hoban, L.C.M.,
Jean Wozniak, Sister Terrence Landini, L.C.M.,
Sister M. Magdalen Nolan, L.C.M. and Paul Wozniak

1982 – Physicians' Awards Dinner
Dr. Paul Lawler, Dr. Robert Craven,
Dr. Zenon Krol and Dr. Joseph Koczur

September, 1987 (left to right)
Marie P. Patricoski, Sister Kathleen McIntyre, L.C.M.
and Ellen McIntyre, Sister Kathleen's mother at the
LCM Auxiliary Membership Tea

Remembering the . . .
1980s

Auxiliary Members - (left to right)
Marge Brosnan, Jean O'Neal, Honor Green, Mary Lou Langdon, Marion Ruzich, Lorrie Craven,
Marion Falloon, Betty Corcoran, LaVerne Sacks and Gloria Farrell

Medical Staff Awards Dinner- Physicians honored,
Earl Vondrasek, M.D., William B. Knapp, M.D.,
Frank J. Doyle, M.D., Joseph Koczur, M.D.
John F. O'Brien, M.D., John J. McLaughlin, M.D.
and Robert P. Meany, M.D.

Monsignor Thomas Obrycki in the Hospital Chapel

From her earliest days on the Hospital staff, Dr. Lourdes D. Floro has been an advocate for children. As noted in an article in *Today's Chicago Women*, "In an adult world filled with high tension, stress and eating disorders, symptoms of these problems manifested in children are often overlooked, but not by Dr. Floro. Beginning in 1972, she initiated and revitalized unique programs designed specifically for youngsters."

1980s
Lourdes D. Floro, M.D.

As a working mother, Dr. Floro knew the difficulties in dealing with sick children when mothers have to work. As more and more mothers took jobs outside the home, they often faced the dilemma of either missing work or finding alternate care if a child became ill. And so it was that the Care Depot, the first of its kind in the area, was created at Little Company in 1987. The eight-bed unit in the pediatrics department was earmarked for the care of sick children, with charges on an hourly basis.

Little Company received an award of merit for the Care Depot in 1988, conferred by the Catholic Health Association of the United States. The Hospital was cited for its "wonderful example of matching the promotional effort to the program's size and potential impact, and creative utilization of budget funds." The CHA also noted that the Care Depot was "clearly founded on the institution's desire to be of public service. With little or no financial gain for the institution, the image of being caring, compassionate and concerned came 'shining through.'

"As someone who was born and raised in the Beverly area, it was through my frequent visits to the Emergency Department and family and friends, that I came to know the Sisters and Little Company of Mary Hospital as a place that provided special care, comfort and compassion to all those in need. I studied at the University of Illinois, and during my residency at Loyola Medical School and internship at Lutheran General Hospital, I knew that one day I would work with the Sisters and share in the Little Company of Mary mission of caring. In June of 1987, I was accepted as a member of the Little Company of Mary Hospital Medical Staff, and I am now very proud to serve as their President. The Sisters and the Hospital are a big part of my many happy memories of family, community and caring. My special thanks to the Sisters for their inspiration and compassionate care to all."

– John P. Hanlon, M.D.,
President of the Professional Staff

1982 - Service Awards Dinner

"More than 20 years ago, I accepted the position of Patient Service Coordinator along with Sister Joseph Casey, L.C.M. Together, we spent 10 years working and laughing together. The employees viewed our job in many different ways as we made visits to patients, employees and visitors. These happy years were supported by our local community which included our most senior Sisters. Among these memorable characters was an outstanding woman, Sister Agnes O'Neill, L.C.M. Sister Agnes spent her retirement years in the mail room until she could no longer stand on her feet. I will never forget her incredible love, loyalty and dedication to Little Company of Mary Hospital. Although no one ever wanted her to over-extend herself, nothing stopped Sister Agnes, even when the snow was up to her knees. As I remember her, I believe that as we stand today it is because of people like Sister, as well as our physicians' and employees' dedication and loyalty, that 70 great years are being celebrated."

— Sister Jean Marsden, L.C.M.

In 1989, the Little Company of Mary Associates program came to the Chicago area. It had begun as a pilot program in 1987, in Laguna Hills, California, and provided an opportunity for Catholic women and men to earnestly strive to live their baptismal commitment and to be closely identified with the spirituality and mission of the Little Company of Mary Sisters.

Their Foundress Venerable Mary Potter had encouraged such affiliations. "They will be glad to join the ranks of those who are banded together in one grand company, to ensure their salvation, to have a part in God's Church," she wrote.

It was not to be a second order, she said. "Let us call it one order, one company of Mary. We, in the convent are the Little Company of Mary, the other the greater. We have, as we have said, the heart animating the whole of the Company our Lady has drawn to herself of all nations. This vast Company must look to us for help and must receive it. They must be tended, cared for, thought for. We must be one, essentially one . . ."

Most candidates for the program were invited or recommended by a Sister of the Little Company of Mary after a long-term association with one or more of the Sisters. Initially, candidates attended six monthly meetings in a study of the life and writings of Mary Potter to learn the spirit and charisma of the Little Company of Mary, Marian spirituality and the Prayer for the Dying. The Associates, as companions of Mary, did not profess canonical vows and undertook no binding financial or legal commitments with the community. Standing with Mary, the model of faithful discipleship, Associates and Sisters of the Little Company of Mary sought to acquire those virtues that would lead them to act justly, love tenderly and walk humbly with their God. (Micah 6:8) The Associates program flourishes today in California and Evergreen Park, with Associates renewing their commitment annually.

Also in 1989, the Hospital began planning the creation of a substance abuse unit. The Illinois Health Facilities Planning Board approved the Hospital's request to convert vacant space on the fourth floor into a 30-bed treatment center for drug and alcohol abuse.

1982 – Auxiliary members Jill Fitzgerald, Helene Nesypor and Therese Kloak, President

Little Company of Mary Associates

Pictured: Mary Jo Quick, Mary Jane O'Sullivan, Cheryl Conroy, Mary Jo May, Joan Murphy, Carol Andrews, Sister Jean Stickney, L.C.M., Lina Mooth, Edna Wooding, Gloria Wentz, Sister Joseph Casey, L.C.M., Mary Lou Zidek, Betty Norris, Virginia Bellisle, Patricia Skarzynski, Ron Skarzynski, Theresa Walsh, Gerry Spatz, and Sister Mary Jane Feil, L.C.M.

Not pictured: Betty Cocoran, Betty DeTamble, Una Donnersberger, Marie Evans, Joyce Farrell, John and Marion Hastings, Barbara Lusk, Beatrice Lyons, Joan Murray, Marge Phelan, Clara Rock and Fran Walls

Sister Kathleen McIntyre, L.C.M., Andrea, Taylor, Judy and Keith Sonichsen

"When I arrived in 1982, it was a return to my roots. I was born at Little Company and growing up I witnessed the commitment my aunt, Sister Felix, made to the sick and dying in her Little Company of Mary ministry. Soon I joined the Sisters, and after a time in California, I returned to Evergreen Park, first to the School of Nursing and then to the Hospital in 1985. As President of Little Company of Mary since 1987, I have journeyed with physicians and nurses, caregivers, auxilians, volunteers, benefactors and countless other friends of the Hospital. I am in awe of their contribution to our healing ministry and forever grateful that they are with us as members of the Greater Company."

— *Sister Kathleen McIntyre, L.C.M., President*

1990s

1 - Aerial view, late 1990s. 2 - Breaking ground for Cancer Center, 1999. 3 - Baby Alumni Reunion, Evergreen Plaza.
4 - Mobile Medical Care continues the Sisters' mission of caring for the sick in their homes. 5 - Monsignor Obrycki Physical Therapy Center, 1999.
6 - Sister Nancy Boyle, L.C.M., leaves a legacy of caring to our "Greater Company of Mary."
7 - Little Company of Mary Sisters celebrate 100 years of service in America with Joseph Cardinal Bernardin.
8 - Little Company of Mary Associates carry on the mission of the Sisters. 9 - Health Education Center in Chicago Ridge Mall.
10 - The Mary Potter Physicians Pavilion is dedicated.
11 - The Little Company of Mary Sisters have emulated their Foundress, Venerable Mary Potter, by caring for the sick and dying in three centuries.

Chapter 7
Community Outreach
1990-2000

The decade began with a celebration of Little Company's 60 years of service to the community. The "Night of the Stars" honored Little Company's family of physicians and the contributions they made to Little Company's rich history.

This formal celebration event was the precursor to Little Company's Crystal Heart Ball, honoring the recipient of the Mary Potter Humanitarian Award and the Sister Nancy Boyle Award for Excellence. The Mary Potter Humanitarian Award is presented annually at the Crystal Heart Ball to honor individuals who embody the vision, mission and spirit of Venerable Mary Potter:

Sister Kathleen McIntyre, L.C.M. and Sister Nancy Boyle, L.C.M.

James W. West, M.D.	*1991*
Sister Rosemary Connelly, R.S.M.	*1992*
Reverend Raymond C. Baumhart, S.J.	*1993*
Wally Phillips	*1994*
Matt and Rose Lamb	*1995*
Christopher Zorich	*1996*
Deloris Jordan	*1997*
Monsignor Ignatius D. McDermott	*1998*
Richard H. Driehaus	*1999*
Sister Catherine Mary Norris, D.C.	*2000*

The Sister Nancy Boyle Award for Excellence was first presented in 1999, and honors an individual or program that personifies the legacy and life of Sister Nancy Boyle, L.C.M., so that her spirit will live on to inspire others. The Award for Excellence has been presented to:

The Heart Connection	*1999*
George J. Cullen	*2000*

Peg Schneider, Chaplain, receiving the 1999 Sister Nancy Boyle Award for Excellence on behalf of the Heart Connection from Foundation Board Chairperson Thomas Bridgman.

"*I remember fondly talking to and being a friend of Sister Damian Young, a great lady, and Sister Nancy Boyle, during the last days of her illness and her determination to attend the Crystal Heart Ball.*"

– *Michael Schneider, Hospital Board of Directors*

A Time To Remember . . .

Eileen and Vince Gavin, Chairpersons
of the first Crystal Heart Ball

Crystal Heart Ball Raffle Ladies

The Crystal Heart Ball 1991
Sister Kathleen McIntyre, L.C.M.,
Cardinal Joseph Bernardin and Dr. and Mrs. James West

The Crystal Heart Ball 1998 – George Cullen, Sister Kathleen
McIntyre, L.C.M., the Honorable Abraham Lincoln Marovitz,
Lourdes D. Floro, M.D., Sister Carol Pacini, L.C.M.,
Rodrigo B. Floro, M.D. and Monsignor Ignatius D. McDermott

Mary Potter Humanitarians
(Left to right) James W. West, M.D., 1991,
Rose and Matt Lamb, 1995,
Sister Rosemary Connelly, R.S.M., 1992,
Reverend Raymond C. Baumhart, S.J., 1993
and Wally Phillips, 1994

The Crystal Heart Ball 2000
(Left to right) Sister Catherine Mary Norris, D.C., 2000 Mary
Potter Humanitarian, Sister Jean Stickney, L.C.M.,
Sister Kathleen McIntyre, L.C.M., Frederick Wohlberg, M.D.,
Nan Hallenbeck, Stephen Hallenbeck, Marilyn Wohlberg
and Sister Margaret Christina Hoban, L.C.M.

Crystal Heart Ball

Richard Driehaus, 1999 Mary Potter Humanitarian, and George Cullen, Vice Chair, Hospital Board of Directors

Deloris Jordan, 1997 Mary Potter Humanitarian, and Sister Kathleen McIntyre, L.C.M.

Frank Schaffer, Chairman of the Board

"I have always viewed Little Company of Mary Hospital as an extended part of my family, having grown up within two miles of the Hospital and having served as a member of its active staff for 25 years. The unity and spirit of the medical staff have never been better and this is due to the coordinated efforts, professionalism and dedication of our entire LCM team beginning with the Little Company of Mary Sisters and filtering down to the nurses, care givers and all employees of the Hospital. As a medical staff, we are all extremely enthusiastic about the new Cancer Center. I am certain that with the continued fervor of the entire LCM team, our institution will continue to flourish in our wonderful community."

– Frederick E. Wohlberg, M.D.

(left to right) Mike Flannery, Sister Kathleen McIntyre, L.C.M., Sister Rosemary Connelly,1992 Humanitarian and Mike Ditka

Sister Kathleen McIntyre, L.C.M. and Christopher Zorich, 1996 Mary Potter Humanitarian

In the late 1980s and the early 1990s, the Hospital played an active role in reaching out to the community through health education and the promotion of healthy lifestyles. The Women's Wellness Center opened at the Hospital and the annual Women's Wellness Weekends, which began in the mid-'80s, continued.

At the same time, Little Company saw the need for increased senior programs to provide healthcare screenings, assistance with insurance forms, skilled nursing in the home, and education for the prevention of disease. Combined with the evolving Hospice program and Home Health programs, Little Company extended its services beyond the Hospital's walls, reaching out to patients in their homes and in the community. These innovative services for seniors include the Mobile Medical Care Unit, a service designed to send a physician-nurse team to people's homes who are unable to travel to the Hospital for tests and treatment. Connections, another senior program, was initiated to provide health screenings, socialization and assistance in filling out insurance forms.

In 1993, the Little Company of Mary Sisters

*(left to right)
Thomas Bridgman,
Monsignor Raymond Boyle
and George Cullen, 2000
Sister Nancy Boyle Award for
Excellence Awardee*

"All my children were born at Little Company. Our daughter, Patricia, was hospitalized for 40 days when she was three. How considerate and thoughtful all of the nurses, doctors and Sisters were! Receiving the Sister Nancy Boyle Award for Excellence was truly one of the highlights of my life. Sister Nancy touched my life most of all. Every time we were together, she would joke about recommending me for a blue veil."

*– George Cullen, Vice Chairman,
Hospital Board of Directors*

A letter sent to Sister Marianne Herres, L.C.M.

"I am writing this letter to thank all those in the Administration Department at Little Company of Mary Hospital who were responsible for seeing a need and providing an Adult Day Care Center to assist the families of the surrounding area in caring for their relatives who are no longer able to care for themselves. And, as I like to feel useful, while my family is at work all day, I come to the Center and help out in many different kinds of ways. The Center provides a variety of good lunches and snacks during the day and there's always something going on by way of activities."

celebrated the 100th anniversary of the founding of their congregation. Sister Nancy Boyle, L.C.M., Provincial Superior of the Little Company of Mary Sisters, recalled Venerable Mary Potter's many references to the 'Greater' Little Company of Mary. "She said that although our numbers may be small, the Greater Little Company is made up of the lay people who embrace the Little Company mission. The legacy of the pioneering Sisters who nurtured the mission with unconditional love through its simple beginnings in America, endures today through the empowerment of others," said Sister Nancy. "The few have become thousands. The mission lives through the Little Company family of Sisters, doctors, nurses, caregivers, employees, volunteers and benefactors."

Mobile Medical Care Unit

"Little Company of Mary Hospital has been the home of my emergency medical practice for the majority of my 20-year career. I have been lucky and I am proud to be a part of this ministry of health care that started 70 years ago. Let us work together to continue this tradition."

– Michael P. O'Mara, D.O.

"My first impression was that Little Company of Mary Hospital was a friendly, caring place where employees cared for one another. I feel a sense of stability when I see the LCM Sisters at Mass."

– Mary Freyer, Director of Resource Management, Case Management, and Employee Education and Training

Sister Nancy Boyle, L.C.M.

"The Sisters have passed on to each of us the mission of Mary Potter. Each of us that has the privilege of working here interprets the mission in a way to best serve those who come here. This Hospital has become my life's work. I never thought of it that way 35 years ago. This has been a vocation and I can honestly say that each day is a good day. Being in the service of others brings new meaning to your life each day."

– Joan Murphy, R.N., Ph.D., Director of Public Relations and Health Promotions

American Province of Little Company of Mary Sisters

The Mary Potter Medical Office Pavilion was dedicated in 1993 to provide office space for physicians affiliated with the Hospital as well as easily accessible Hospital services for their patients. A new Pediatric Critical Care Unit opened and the pediatrics floor was redecorated through contributions given by Hospital employees and other benefactors.

Little Company's commitment to the health of its community involves more than caring for the sick and dying. Part of that commitment also involves promoting health and wellness to prevent illness. In 1994, a wise and forward-thinking Sister Margaret Christina Hoban commissioned an assessment of the surrounding community's health status to help determine where Little Company should focus its efforts. It was out of this Evergreen Park Health Assessment that Sister Margaret Christina brought together the "Healthier Evergreen" committee.

"Healthier Evergreen," a catalyst for positive, healthy lifestyle changes, is a partnership supported by Mayor Anthony Vacco and the Evergreen Park Police and Fire Departments, and consists of Little Company physicians and nurse educators and business leaders. The committee, which began in 1995, has met periodically to form goals and action plans to make Evergreen Park a healthier community.

"If babies could have memories – my happiest memory of Little Company would be when I was born here 70 years ago."

— *Sister Mary Jane Feil, L.C.M.*

" I remember when I was a student and worked on Christmas Eve. I was in pediatrics, holding a sick child and looking out the window as a gentle snow began to fall. People were walking to midnight Mass. I knew I was in the right place. The Sisters have been my mentors, my teachers and my friends."

— *Marie F. Ruff, R.N.,*
Vice President, Patient Care Services

Thoughts from . . .

Sister Magdalen Nolan, L.C.M.

"In the 1960s we developed a 25-bed rehabilitation unit in the Three North area which was led and directed by Dr. Arthur Rodriguez and Dr. Joseph Koczur, Doctors of Physical Medicine. It was a self-contained unit staffed with trained and competent care givers. Patients cared for were those who had physical, neurological and orthopaedic disabilities with limited functional abilities. The local and city health departments provided social services. To alleviate frustrations and hopelessness that many patients felt about their condition, we had movies, patients bowling down the corridor, birthday parties and various forms of entertainment. Joseph Burger and his physical therapists were a vital part of our service. Mary Jane O'Sullivan, Ethel Misuraca and Nancy Neuman represent the great nursing staff who were noted for their kind, compassionate nursing care which is a trademark of our Hospital. Paul Kukel and Monsignor Obrycki were two of the first patients to come into the unit. Mr. Kukel and his family still keep in touch to this day. This department represented the work of many individuals whose talents were vitally important to our growth over the years. The work of these dedicated souls allows us to look ahead for another 70 years.

My personal and professional life has been closely interwoven in the growth and development of our LCM in Evergreen Park since the early 1940s. It begins with being a member of our LCM Religious Community, attending the Hospital School of Nursing from 1943-46 and serving in various positions within the institution. This relationship was broken at times with assignments in other locations. My first memory of LCM was that of a single free-standing four-story building located in an open and undeveloped area just a few blocks west of Western Avenue. It seemed to be so remote — a rather isolated area — lacking sufficient pavement so some areas were rather muddy when it rained. It's hard to believe today that it was considered to be an unfavorable site for a hospital — almost too far out to come for hospitalization or to visit patients. Many considered this venture of the Sisters to be very risky business and could not visualize it amounting to much."

"I think it is very evident that 'the Greater Company of Mary' — employees, physicians, volunteers — have embraced the Mission of Mary Potter as our own. We are committed to serving the needs of this community — the physical, emotional and spiritual needs — and we will do this as we have for the past 70 years — integrating our knowledge and skill with compassion, faith and prayer."

— Mary Jo Quick, R.N., Director, Mission and Values Integration

"When we lost our beloved son, Chuck, who was 23 years old, I can't even begin to describe the pain. Little Company of Mary's pastoral care program helped me get through the worst time of my life. Being in a group where we all were suffering the loss of our children helped us understand we were not alone. Your program made a difference in my life and I was able to come to terms with the loss of our son."

— Carol A. Manganiello

Mayor Anthony Vacco of Evergreen Park
and Frank Schaffer

A letter to Doctors Richard Farrell, Thomas Quinn, Kelly Guglielmi, Dean Govostis and John Zumerchik:

"Without the expertise, caring, knowledge and sincere concern of all of you, as a team, working together, my hubby, Robert Stroh, would probably not be alive. Thanks for all the years you have spent learning to cure the ills of your patients and for giving your time and knowledge to the sick. Little Company of Mary is the greatest."

— Joy Stroh and family

"Shortly after I completed nurses' training, I had an experience that shaped my life. I was working on the 3-11 shift — a young Sister who thought being busy and doing were the important things, as I rustled up and down the halls in my white, starched gown. On the floor was a young patient about 31. She was married and had a small child. Her room was off the rotunda across from the desk. She had just found out she had cancer. I walked into the room one evening and said, 'Can I do anything for you?' She said, 'What can you do for a broken heart?' All I could do was sit on the edge of the bed and hold her in my arms, while we both cried. I learned that night 'doing' isn't always the important thing. Sometimes there is nothing one can do except just 'be present.' So often it seems, only in one's vulnerability and helplessness is one able to be present to others and be with others. Each time I pass one of those rotunda rooms now, I am reminded of her and remember her with a prayer. I am grateful for this lesson that I learned during my ministry at Little Company in Evergreen Park, because it has been such a help in my active ministry. It is especially meaningful now as I grow older and activity wanes because of loss of energy, and I realize that presence to and being with God and others in God becomes all important."

— Sister Virginia O'Brien, L.C.M.

In 1995, after calling the Hospital his home since 1951, Chaplain Emeritus Monsignor Thomas Obrycki died. The *Chicago Tribune* described his healing work over the years as follows: "There is no anger, grief or envy in his words. There is only that sense of peace and joy, as though a great battle no other man can fully grasp were over and won." Monsignor Obrycki was a man whose faith and service reached beyond his physical limitations and he was an inspirational presence in the physical therapy department for more than four decades. Fittingly, in 1997, the Hospital dedicated its new physical therapy center, and named it the Thomas Obrycki Physical Therapy Center.

(left to right) Robert Mueller,
Monsignor Obrycki and Fran Gallagher

September 1996 – (left to right)
Sister Kathleen McIntyre, L.C.M., President,
Thomas Bridgman, Foundation Board Chairman and
Campaign Chairman, Sister Carol Pacini, L.C.M.
and Al O'Malley, Campaign Co-Chairman

Recognizing the challenges faced by all non-profit hospitals in the Chicagoland area, the Sisters and a cadre of dedicated volunteers came together to evaluate the Hospital's fundraising activities in the mid-1990s. Sister Kathleen McIntyre, Little Company's president and CEO, enlisted this leadership group to establish the Little Company of Mary Hospital Foundation. Community and business leaders were invited to join its Board of Directors and support the Hospital's mission through raising funds to enhance services, purchase needed equipment and provide for mission-driven and community-based services. The group enthusiastically worked together with Hospital administration to identify areas of the Hospital in need of philanthropic support.

"From one who learns better by 'hands on' experience, by 'doing' rather than by just observing or studying about something, I realize how rewarding my nursing career has been because of the invaluable experiences I had as a student in the Hospital's three-year diploma nursing program and the many experiences that I had while working at LCM as a new graduate. As a new R.N. who had just transferred from the fifth floor MICU, my greatest fear was my first 'Dr. Standby' (AKA Code Blue). However, my first night off orientation and as charge nurse, one of the patients was in great distress. It was traumatic, but taught me so much. Needless to say, the next night when I did have a 'Dr. Standby,' it was a breeze, a piece of cake."

– Sister Renee Cunningham, L.C.M.

"I have been at Little Company in Evergreen Park for the past fifty years in service to our community, and I am grateful for these years of ministry to God's people."

– Sister Margaret Christina Hoban, L.C.M.

Thoughts from . . .

Sister Mary John Schlax, L.C.M.

"When I entered our Little Company of Mary Community in 1942, the Hospital was a four-story building and only 12 years old, standing in the country. There was nothing between the Hospital and the Western Avenue streetcar line except the corner hot dog stand, a vegetable stand, Shalks Bowling Alley and sidewalks running only part of way on either side of the street. In 1944, I was introduced to the Hospital's Business Office where Sister Virginia was in charge. There were only a few employees and Margaret Connors was the person who took care of all the patient insurance groups.

My first assignment was to balance accounts receivable — all entries were hand written then. Before long, we became quite modern when a machine for entering and balancing our daily records was purchased! After I was professed, I was in charge of the Business Office and Sister Agnes was in charge of the Admission Office.

Later, the Credit and Collection Department expanded under the direction of Edward Newmes, whom I hired. As time went on, Mr. Hudson and Mr. Hibbott, excellent people, were hired. As the Accounting Department was growing, Ron Skarzynski was in charge there, and Mr. Conlon managed Admissions and Accounts Receivable. We were truly blessed with good and reliable people.

In 1964, I went on assignment to Rome, and Mr. Hibbott was appointed treasurer of the Hospital by our Provincial, Mother Oliver. She was a woman of wisdom. I thoroughly enjoyed my years at the Hospital and am always interested in hearing of its developments and growth. Today, it has come a long way from the four floors when I first came to Evergreen Park! I pray for Sister Kathleen and all the people along the way through these many years who have done so much in responding to the Hospital's mission and growth. May God continue to generously bless all those and their families who have been or are presently bringing the healing presence of Christ to those who come through its doors!"

"My first experience working in the Hospital was when Sister Mary John Schlax, L.C.M. was Supervisor of the business office. After two years of religious training I began working in the Hospital. Because I had a business background when I came to the Order, I was placed under Sister Mary John's wing--so to speak. I got to know all the wonderful women as I moved about from desk to desk learning the different workings in the office.
Ron Skarzynski, who later became Vice President of Finance, started working at Little Company around the same time. Some of the great ladies who were imbued with the spirit of Mary Potter were Colette Dolorn, Helene Ruplankis, Bea Sendlock, Doris Peterson and Edna Cooling. Some are resting in God's arms today. I look back with fond memories of the marvelous people who have journeyed with us during these 70 years. The have touched our lives and we are the better for it."

– Sister Kay Shalvey, L.C.M.

1999 – Little Company of Mary Hospital Foundation Board
Wendy Drynan, Gloria Jackson, Linda Crane, Marilyn Wohlberg, Sheila Yakutis, Sister Joseph Casey, L.C.M., Michael Toolis,
Lawrence P. Kelley, Sister Kathleen McIntyre, L.C.M., Thomas F. Bridgman, Marci Schneider Batsakis, Lourdes D. Floro, M.D.,
Martin J. McLaughlin, Ald. Ginger Rugai, Mary Jo May. Not pictured: Mary Ann Fitzgerald, Basel I. Al-Aswad, M.D.,
Howard Brookins, Sr., George Cullen, Dr. Elnora D. Daniel, Thomas Dombro, Sr., Donna Gellatly, Linda Hartz,
Sister Margaret Christina Hoban, L.C.M., Sheila Kelly, James A.K. Lambur, M.D., Anthony Lepore,
Homer Livingston, Jr., John J. McCormack, William Mulcahy, Steven Rosenbaum, Frank Schaffer, Sr. and Ralph Steinbarth

Foundation Board Chair Thomas F. Bridgman of Beverly led the Board as they evaluated suggestions and boldly began *"Our Work of Love: The Campaign for Little Company of Mary Hospital and Health Care Centers."* The capital campaign, co-chaired by Mr. Bridgman and Alfred J. O'Malley, Chairman of Standard Bank & Trust Company, would provide funds for outpatient services, a new physical therapy area, One-Day Surgery Unit and a new Cancer Center. Funds were also earmarked to build an endowment fund for mission-driven services needed by the community, such as support groups, grief counseling for children and adults facing the loss of a loved one, Hospice, senior services such as adult day care and mobile medicine, health education and charity care.

"Sister Kathleen is an inspiring leader of the Hospital and its Foundation. Her strong leadership and good humor affirm the work of the Foundation as we build relationships and raise funds so that Little Company can continue to provide high quality, compassionate care to all who enter the Hospital's doors now and in the future," said Mr. Bridgman.

In 1997, at its Reflections annual dinner and fashion show, the Little Company of Mary Hospital Auxiliary announced its support for *Our Work of Love*, joining countless other benefactors.

Foundation Board Members James A.K. Lambur, M.D. and Thomas Bridgman

The Auxiliary has a long tradition of generous support for Hospital programs to benefit patients and their families through events such as Reflections, the Holiday House Walk, the 2800 Gift Shop and the Hospice and Tribute Funds. The Auxiliary belongs to the Illinois Hospital and Health Systems Association Council of Volunteers, providing opportunities for Auxilians to attend educational meetings each year, enhancing their leadership skills and sharing ideas with other hospital auxiliaries.

"It was a great privilege for me to have served as the General Chairperson of the Auxiliary of Little Company of Mary Hospital. The Auxiliary is an organization of dedicated individuals who willingly donate their time, talents and support toward the betterment of Little Company of Mary Hospital and its many patients and their families. Besides supporting Little Company financially by raising funds for the new Cancer Center, the Auxiliary is a constant visual presence in the Hospital for all those who walk its halls. The future of Little Company of Mary is bright due to its visionary Sisters, its excellent staff of dedicated doctors and nurses, its committed administration and its many devoted employees and volunteers, among whom the Auxiliary proudly stands."

— Marilyn Wohlberg, Auxilian

"Working in Nursing at Little Company of Mary Hospital has helped me keep things in perspective. It has given me a good sense of what is important and what is fleeting."

— Sister Maura Tangney, L.C.M.

"Over the past 20 years I have journeyed with the Little Company of Mary Sisters and I have been enriched by their spirit, their ministry and their care and compassion."

— Thomas Murray, Hospital Board of Directors

"Working at LCM was one of the best things that ever happened to me. My favorite memories include employee Christmas parties, the Auxiliary's Garnet Ball, trips to Notre Dame and listening to actor Pat O'Brien tell some of his famous Irish stories."

— Francis X. Gallagher

1999 – Auxiliary Membership Dinner
Jack Simmerling, Sister Kathleen McIntyre, L.C.M.,
Jill Fitzgerald, Wayne Wolf and Marilyn Wohlberg

Prompted by the initiatives of "Healthier Evergreen," and supported by the Hospital's Mission Committee, the Hospital's focus on health education and outreach to the community intensified. In 1996, the Hospital's first Education Center was opened in Chicago Ridge Mall, to bring education to people outside the walls of the Hospital. Two years later, the second Health Education Center opened its doors in Evergreen Plaza. Countless men, women and children have attended educational programs, received a relaxing massage or learned more about their own or their family's health through Little Company's healing presence.

By the 1990s, Little Company's "baby alumni" numbered upwards of 190,000. In an effort to bring some of its distinguished offspring together, the first Little Company of Mary Hospital Baby Alumni Reunion was held at Evergreen Plaza in the fall of 1997. Beverly native George Wendt of "Cheers" fame and son of loyal Auxilian Loret Wendt was on hand to visit fellow alums.

"My first introduction to LCM was applying for a nurse's aide job. It was the summer of my sophomore year in high school. I arrived at LCM on a Saturday afternoon. Sister M. Fidelis asked me a few questions and sent me to the sixth floor where Sister M. Camille greeted me and said I could not work in a broomstick skirt, peasant blouse and high heels. A few more questions were asked and Sister M. Camille said, 'I can use you on my floor. Report for duty tomorrow morning.' I hurried home and on Sunday morning at 7 a.m. donned a white uniform. I began my job and happy life with LCM. My Sister supervisors on the sixth floor were Sisters Camille, Francis and Perpetua. I observed their dedication, commitment and patient-centered service. The linen room keys were on a long chain and many a one-on-one conference was held in the linen room by Sister Perpetua. The linen room saw more than neatly folded sheets—it held many pearls of truth and wisdom from a compassionate, concerned and caring woman who gave her best and desired the same for all of us—Sister M. Perpetua."

— Sister Deborah A. Conley, L.C.M.

1993 - Carol Andrews and Jack Faber, representing the Mary Potter Employee Crisis Fund, receive a donation from members of the Employee Giving Steering Committee. (Left to right) Linda Cantu, Dennis Reilly, Marie Moore, George Sapienza, Joan Murphy, Tony Lukcevic, Jack Faber and Carol Andrews

Thoughts from . . .

Sister Mildred Radziewicz, L.C.M.

"My first experience working at Little Company of Mary was as a novice in 1959, and working as a general duty nurse. In the next few years after profession, I worked in almost every area of the Hospital. My favorite department was Obstetrics and I saw many precious little ones born in my time. Sometimes, they came one in eight hours and sometimes eight in eight hours or less. We had a marvelous staff of obstetricians: Drs. Lawler, Blough, Gorman, McCready and many others, supported by wonderful residents like Drs. Cava and Jagodzinski and others. Especially treasured is the efficiency of the staff and the lasting friendships with Ginnie Kavanaugh, Millie Eckroth, Mrs. Horachek, Mary Smith, Mrs. Teeter and others who are no longer with us.

I left Evergreen Park in 1965, and when I returned, I was in quite a different role as Chairman of the Board, which presented new challenges and responsibilities. But I realized that we have always had wonderful people with us whose prime interest and decisions were made for the success of Little Company of Mary Hospital and the people we serve. I also had days of great joy working with the Auxiliary, many dedicated women who did much to provide funds through their numerous activities like 'Reflections,' always a beautiful and successful event. Another exciting event was the great Country Fair we planned out on the Hospital's front lawn. I was surprised when Carol Andrews invited some bag pipers in their Scottish dress to entertain outside, and then go into the Hospital. All went well, and the patients really enjoyed the music. I am grateful to God for knowing all these wonderful people and having the privilege of working with them to make our LCM the best it could be in providing loving and compassionate care to all who come to us. The present has been built on the dedication of all who have served in the past. May God bless them!"

The Sisters of the Little Company of Mary at the 70th Anniversary Celebration of the Hospital

A Time To Remember . . .
Baby Alumni

The Baby Alumni Party at the Evergreen Plaza

Joan Murphy and Loret Wendt

George Wendt with Sister Kathleen McIntyre, L.C.M.

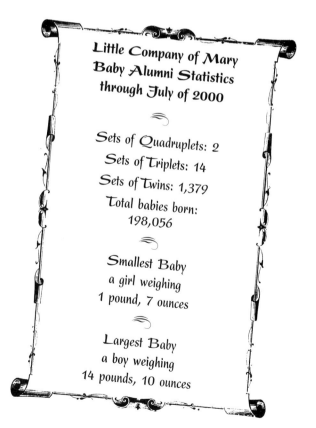

**Little Company of Mary
Baby Alumni Statistics
through July of 2000**

Sets of Quadruplets: 2
Sets of Triplets: 14
Sets of Twins: 1,379
Total babies born:
198,056

Smallest Baby
a girl weighing
1 pound, 7 ounces

Largest Baby
a boy weighing
14 pounds, 10 ounces

In 1998, the Sisters' original stained-glass windows from their first convent on Indiana Avenue were removed and brought to Little Company through the generous response of the many friends of Sister Nancy Boyle. Charles Mair, the Sisters' first benefactor in America, had commissioned the windows for their first chapel in 1899, and when the Sisters moved to Evergreen Park in 1930, the windows remained at 41st and Indiana. The treasured windows, dedicated to Sister Nancy Boyle, now reside in the newly restored original entrance to the Hospital.

The same year, Little Company's Wound Care Center opened, offering a multi-disciplinary approach to healing chronic wounds, using hyperbaric oxygen chambers and featuring an oxygen-based treatment and the other resources needed to treat wounds that do not respond to conventional methods.

Sister Nancy Boyle's family at the dedication of the stained glass windows

Dennis Reilly, Vice President/Chief Operating Officer and Lawrence Kelley, Foundation Board Vice Chairperson

"I felt that Little Company gave so much to our community that I should serve LCM in this great endeavor. The Hospital stands as a monument of strength and compassion that is here to serve our community when needed. Working with Sister Kathleen, you can't help but feel a sense of fulfillment in serving the mission of the Sisters to the Lord. I am proud for helping guide the Hospital."

— Frank Schaffer, Chairman of the Board

"The Sisters' dedication to their mission most impressed me. And how happy they were when they obtained the stained glass windows from their first chapel at 4130 South Indiana Avenue."

— Francis X. Gallagher

"My Dad, Dr. Warren Furey, used to bring me to the Hospital while he was reading x-rays. I remember Mass in the chapel and meeting with the Sisters for treats."

— Ginnie Lawler

LCM Sisters original stained glass windows

LCM Sisters
Sister Kathleen McIntyre, L.C.M., Sister Deborah Conley, L.C.M.,
Sister Catherine Shalvey, L.C.M., Sister Virginia O'Brien, L.C.M.,
Sister Sheila Brosnan, L.C.M. and Sister Joseph Casey, L.C.M.

LCM Sisters at the original convent site located at
41st Street and Indiana Avenue with Rev. Louis Rawls

"The Little Company of Mary spirit and mission of compassion and caring for the sick and dying has been nurtured and strengthened through the lived experience of all who have shared the journey with us in these 70 years. The words of Venerable Mary Potter, 'We all have the power within us for doing good,' have compelled us to meet the challenges and opportunities for collaboration with openness and courage. As we celebrate the gifts and blessings of all who shared in this collaborative spirit, let us continue to go forward meeting the needs of those we are called to serve."

— Sister Sharon Ann Walsh, L.C.M.

As the centerpiece of the Hospital Foundation's capital campaign *'Our Work of Love,'* plans for the construction of Little Company's new Cancer Center were finalized and the ground breaking for the new facility took

*Dr. S. Javed Shirazi
with patient*

place in August 1999, with Bishop John Gorman officiating.

"It is a privilege and an honor to work with so many talented volunteers in raising funds for this important project, which will offer the finest cancer diagnosis and treatment options available for our cancer patients and their families," said Mary Jo May, Executive Director of the Little Company of Mary Hospital Foundation. "Campaign Co-Chairs Tom Bridgman and Al O'Malley have been tireless in their support, advice and active participation in *Our Work of Love,* and through their leadership, they are making our new Cancer Center a reality.

Foundation Board members, physicians, employees, and our extended family of community leaders, residents, patients and friends inspire us as they support Little Company's mission and ministry. As a long-time Little Company of Mary volunteer and employee,

*July 1995
Jim Joyce and Dennis Day*

I am truly enriched by my association with friends of the Hospital. I am especially grateful to our Sisters and awed by the example they have been to me."

As an extension of the first-rate treatment already offered at the Hospital, the new Cancer Center will unite all cancer treatment and technologies in one convenient location. The Center, through Little Company's affiliation with the Medical Oncology

"'The Hospital down the street is run by very strict Sisters.' I used to hear that when I was doing my internship elsewhere. After almost 27 years here, I would say, it is run by a family of compassionate, caring, hard working and competent people who want to make a difference in the lives of people that cross their path. I want to thank the Sisters for giving me the opportunity and environment to fulfill my own desires of doing what I like to do best, which is to promote people's health emotionally, physically and with a personal touch. The Sisters of the Little Company of Mary have fully supported my mission as I have tried to support their mission. The new Cancer Center is a testament to the commitment of the Sisters of the Little Company of Mary to provide excellence in care to the community they serve."

— S. Javed Shirazi, M.D.,
Medical Director of Radiation Oncology

"The exciting part of seeing the Cancer Center develop is the realization that the facility will be the culmination of the dreams and hopes of so many people. It will reflect the suggestions of patients, physicians, staff and the Sisters who participated in the planning. Enhanced by the affiliation with the Medical Oncology Group of the University of Chicago Hospitals it will offer state-of-the-art cancer treatment and will do so in a holistic spirit as the Sisters have taught us."

— Dennis Day, *Vice President, Support Services*

"I volunteered for the Humor Outreach Program. Visiting cancer patients was a heart-warming and Christian ministry. It was a challenging and learning experience that showed we are all different, but in some ways are the same. I thought I was doing something for the patients, but the patients were doing something for me — blessing me."

— Joann Filipello, *Auxilian and Volunteer*

Little Company of Mary Hospital's Cancer Center

Group of the University of Chicago Hospitals, will offer convenient cancer treatment for residents of southwest Chicago and the southwest suburbs. Little Company's highly respected radiation oncology unit will continue to be located in the lower level of the Cancer Center.

The Cancer Center will offer a wide range of services such as food and nutrition counseling and pastoral care, and cancer support groups where participants come together to share insights, information and humor to promote healing and coping. A patient advocate will provide information and assistance. The complementary therapies area will offer hypnosis, massage and aromatherapy and consultation on prostheses, skin care and make-up enhancement.

On the ground floor of the Cancer Center, a community resource library will feature easy access to information on cancer through interactive videos, the Internet, journals and other reference materials. The Serenity Room will provide a quiet place for meditation and reflection. Because treating the whole person is a hallmark of Little Company's care, cancer patients will find abundant resources for their medical, emotional and spiritual needs.

The 33,000-square-foot addition will house new

technologies and a host of innovative programs and services–all within a tranquil, light-filled space. A unique aspect of the new Center will be Lina's Care Closet, which is located on the ground floor. Begun by June Crawley of Evergreen Park, and initially operated from her home, the closet provides medical supplies and equipment to patients in treatment for cancer and other long-term illnesses. In 1975, the Care Closet moved to Little Company of Mary. Staffed by Hospital volunteer Lina Mooth, it is one of the few services of its kind on the South Side and southwest suburbs.

Lina Mooth, Volunteer, Cancer Care Closet

In 1999, the Illinois Legislature and the Illinois Secretary of State recognized the Hospital's distinction of performing the first human organ transplant. Secretary of State Jesse White, whose sister was the recipient of a donor kidney, came to the Hospital to address those gathered on the importance of the organ donation program in Illinois.

Thoughts from . . .

Sister Mary Babcock, L.C.M.

"My history with the Little Company of Mary Hospital began in 1956, when I arrived from Boston, Massachusetts and entered the Religious Community of the Sisters of the Little Company of Mary.

I worked in the Radiology Department while I attended the Radiological Technology School, graduating in 1961. Drs. John Brosnan, John Uhrich and Nicholas Beck were on staff and Sister Mary Barbara Snyder was the Religious Supervisor with Sister Sheila Brosnan. I enjoyed my time in radiology; our staff reached out to the patients and were always supportive of one another. They had a great love for LCM.

I would like to recall also my memories when I was in the education department in the early 1980s, when Jim McCampbell was the manager and I worked in diabetic teaching. I worked with Joan Murphy on several projects. Betty Wetzel and I worked on a program for seniors at Mother McAuley High School who were interested in following a career in the medical field. The students who went through the program often came back to report they had chosen careers as physical therapists and x-ray and laboratory technicians.

Another program I found very enriching was sponsored by a grant from the University of Chicago for training nurses in diabetic teaching. Joan Murphy designed the program and scheduled the nurses for teaching diabetics in groups. Patients came down from the units and classes were followed by a question/answer period and time to relate to other patients, creating an informal support group. I feel privileged to have worked with so many wonderful and dedicated people and for the care and concern they had not only for our patients, but also for each other. The Hospital was enriched by all these wonderful people. God bless all!"

"Not only is our 'Spirited Service' program alive and well here at the Hospital, it also thrives in our off-campus facilities and patients' homes through the Oak Lawn Care Station, Burbank Radiology Center, Mobile Medical Care, Home Based Services, Hospice, and Home Health Equipment Center."

– Ann Haskins, Vice President, Business Development

LCM Volunteers
Top Row: Bryon McLaughlin, Jason Sullivan, Jim Hackett, Tony Piet, Jr., John Daley
Middle Row: Mike Dimenn, Julie Dunn, Betty Breshnahan, Dorothy Flanagan, Terese O'Sullivan,
Peg Nottingham, Dorothy Wilcher, Sue Hinkens, Evelyn Samonski
Sitting: Margaret Kapp, Vera Kadich, Marge Rich, Clara Rock, Florence Bejcek and Sophia Weiss

"I am proud to be associated with Little Company of Mary. I was appointed to the medical staff in 1963. The Hospital has an excellent reputation for patient care and residency programs."

– Dr. John Zumerchik

"My fondest memories of Little Company of Mary Hospital are of the births of my two sons. Through these doors emerged my greatest hopes and dreams. Now through volunteering, I am able to repay some of my good fortune and to bring comfort to others. The people and staff are so kind here that I look forward to coming each day."

– Clara Rock, Volunteer

"In the 37 years of my medical practice, health care has changed dramatically. I have been fortunate to have practiced medicine all those years, and I am thankful that I have been God's instrument for healing here at Little Company of Mary."

– Dr. Martin Phee

Thoughts from . . .

Sister Sheila Brosnan, L.C.M.

"Family spirit, team work and dedication have been a way of life at Little Company of Mary in Evergreen Park since I arrived on the scene in the 1950s. It has been my privilege to have ministered in Radiology, Nuclear Medicine, Radiation Therapy and Cobalt for many years, followed up with Pastoral Care and more recently Hospice ministry which embraces our calling as Little Company of Mary Sisters. My years in Radiology were challenging and demanding. Often in the midst of turmoil due to construction and equipment inspection, the famous words were 'we are moving right along,' which helped maintain a degree of sanity and good humor all through the years. We were blessed also with gifted, dedicated radiologists and staff.

At Little Company, family spirit was evident everywhere. On Sunday mornings the doctors arrived, accompanied by their children. While the doctors made rounds, the little ones would play in the lobby, cared for by a Sister. Many of those children are physicians here today. Our Little Company of Mary students in Nursing, Radiology and Medical Technology and many others are carrying on also in the footsteps of their parents. Team work and dedication at Little Company of Mary has been a way of life and can only be accomplished by dedicated, skillful people sharing their expertise and knowledge for the good of all.

Our Sisters who have gone before us had the power within them for doing good and living their lives for God. Our Foundress Venerable Mary Potter always acknowledged the commitment and dedication of the tremendous support the clergy gave to our community all through the years, and I endorse her sentiments. Finally, a favorite saying of our Foundress Venerable Mary Potter was, 'We live in perilous times.' We continue to live in perilous times today. However, you will be pleased to know: We are moving right along."

"Most organizations today have adopted a mission statement which is prominently displayed on an entranceway or in the Board room. What distinguishes Little Company of Mary Hospital from the rest is that the mission isn't just a piece of paper hanging on a wall. The mission is being lived and reinforced by everyone associated with the Hospital. The mission is not an organizational management tool. It is a way of life."

— Steve Hallenbeck, Hospital Board of Directors

"Through my 67 years as a Sister of Little Company of Mary, I have realized the unconditional love of Christ for me and my welfare. Could I do less for others? My life at LCM has been a journey through rocky roads and well-paved highways, but always with love. I have been blessed. It has been a wonderful journey."

— Sister Michael Murray, L.C.M.

"During my 18 years as Medical Director of the Department of Radiology, my overwhelming impression is the extraordinary commitment and the dedication of the Little Company of Mary Sisters to health care. This level of dedication and commitment is found only in a charitable organization like the Sisters have attained."

— George F. Hogan, M.D.

"My earliest recall of the Hospital as an eight-year-old is sitting on the marble steps at the main entrance, which was separated from 95th Street by large trees and fine grass. The doctors could park their cars along the circular drive leading to the impressive two-story entrance hall. After my father made rounds with Sister Helen or Sister Bernadette on the maternity floor, I'd watch him and the other doctors play softball against many interns and residents. They played on the field where the convent now stands. After the War and for another 20 years, LCM was extremely active and rather famous for its very large number of births which sometimes exceeded 500 in a month. Only Cook County Hospital delivered more babies. The Hospital was there at the right time and place as young families migrated to the southwest suburbs. The Sisters were well known for the standard of care they provided as well as their generosity; they never financially pressured their patients. The Hospital was also well known for its excellent medical staff, and it is this staff of which I am so very proud. Not only dedicated healers, they provided many years of leadership to the medical community. When I go by the Hospital now, I remember sweet things like my first glimpses of my own newborns and Christmas Eve masses in the Chapel, where I first met my lovely wife Ginny. Happiness is memories and dreams. I dream that Little Company of Mary continues down the same blessed road for another 70 years."

— Paul Lawler, Jr., M.D.

"My involvement with the Hospital goes back to the days when I was a young boy. Over the years, the care my family and I have received has been superior and compassionate."

— Thomas C. Hynes, 19th Ward Committeeman

"I truly believe that people here work together as a team and care about all facets of the organization. There is a great respect between the non-clinical and clinical areas. We are all here to serve our patients in the best way we can."

— Randy Ruther, Vice President, Finance

Remembering the 1990s . . .

Ron Skarzynski, Marci Batsakis,
Laura Shallow and Sheila Yakutis

Volunteers - (Back row) Dorothy Flanagan, Pauline Roeters,
(Front row) Sophia Weiss, June Ginty, Florence Bejcek,
Marion Phillips and Jeanne Ryan

Cheer Group

1999 – Dr. and Mrs. P.P. Mangrola visit
Sister Kathleen McIntyre, L.C.M.

T. Paul O'Donovan, M.D.

"In 1976 I came to Little Company from Mayo Clinic and worked with Dr. Ralph Zitmik. I was immediately struck with the family atmosphere of the Hospital, the superb nursing staff and the Sisters' dedication to the community. In my 25 years here, I have seen the way Little Company has been able to adapt to the major changes in the medical care field in a very positive and successful way, and I am happy to be a part of its healthcare ministry."

— T. Paul B. O'Donovan, M.D.

As Sister Jean Stickney said on January 19, 2000, in her inspiring remarks to Little Company's employees:

"Today we celebrate the 70th Anniversary of this Hospital's opening its doors to patients in our surrounding communities. It is fitting that we begin this year of celebration here in the Chapel. We celebrate major landmarks and achievements only because of God's innumerable blessings. There have been blessings of generous benefactors, altruistic volunteers, the Associates and Auxiliary members, and committed physicians and staff. There have been blessings of hope and healing to thousands of persons seeking services here. For all these untold blessings, we are grateful to God.

It was in 1993 that we celebrated the 100th anniversary of the Little Company of Mary Sisters coming to America. The theme of the anniversary was a 'Journey of Unconditional Love.' This year our theme is 'Our Journey of Unconditional Love Continues.'

It is our journey, all of us—not only Sisters, but also all who are part of the Greater Company of Mary, each with our own insights and talents. Venerable Mary Potter wrote, 'We all have a power within us for doing good.' That conviction prompted her to seek partners to further her vision and mission of being a healing presence. You embody her dream and are perpetuating it. Let us move forward on the journey toward the milestones yet to be.

Both the old and the new played significant roles in important events as Little Company of Mary Hospital moved into the 1990's and entered the new millennium."

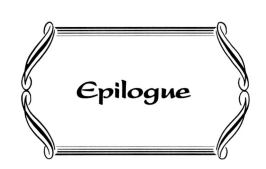

Epilogue

"After 70 years, our journey of unconditional love continues. As we welcome a new millennium, we reflect on the faith-filled journey when our founding Sisters extended the healing ministry of our Foundress, Venerable Mary Potter, from the small convent on 41st Street and Indiana Avenue to the four-story hospital in Evergreen Park.

Our caring tradition was the propelling force that led our Foundress Venerable Mary Potter, to establish our Congregation in 1877, which is devoted to prayer and care of the sick and dying, and it is what brought our six Sisters to Chicago on the steamship from Italy in 1893. Today, 70 years later, Christ's healing mission continues as a testament to those dedicated and tireless Sisters.

In planning and building this new Hospital, the Sisters had a vision filled with joy and hope in times of uncertainty. They were united in prayer with the Lord. Since the Hospital opened its doors, Little Company has been a place of comfort and prayerful support, offering hope to countless patients and families. The Sisters have been faithful and faith-filled in meeting numerous challenges, largely because of their 'companions along the way,' the Greater Company of Mary.

Little Company of Mary Hospital has greatly expanded its healthcare ministries because of the special people in our lives – scores of dedicated and compassionate professionals. We are especially grateful for our partnership with Little Company physicians – men and women of skill, integrity and dedication. Our nurses and caregivers at the bedside and all our support staff are empowered by the mission of our Foundress to embody the healing presence of Jesus. We gratefully acknowledge the 'Charles Mairs' of today and tomorrow, generous benefactors who transform our vision of bringing the highest quality health care to our patients and community into a reality.

Little Company begins its journey into the 21st century with faith, a vision and a Christ-centered ministry. We are heartened by the knowledge that lay members of our healthcare family are empowered to carry on the mission of our pioneering Sisters into the future.

Finally, we invite you to walk side-by-side with us on our journey of unconditional love. We ask that you join us in a prayer of gratitude for all that has been and in petition to God that this Hospital continues to be a source of hope and healing for all who seek our care."

– Sister Kathleen McIntyre, L.C.M., President

"There is no greater power in life than Love."

– Venerable Mary Potter

A Family Tradition

Is Medicine Contagious?

A Family Tradition of Physicians at Little Company

The years of service given by our physicians and their sons and daughters who followed them, spans generations and adds up to hundreds of years. We thank them and pay tribute to their families for the extraordinary example they have given us.

The McGrath Family
Harold F., Sr. and Harold F., Jr.

The Farrell Family
William, Sr., William J., Brian, and Richard

The Soltes Family
Francis J. and Steven J.

The Oliveri Family
Daniel W., John F. and Michael J.

The McCarthy Family
Martin and William D.

The Zumerchik Family
John and David L.

The O'Reilly Family
Clarence J., William S. and Daniel J.

The O'Donoghue Family
John B., Sr., John, Jr., and Michael J.

The Lawler Family
Edmund G., Thomas P., Paul, Sr., Paul, Jr., Richard and Frank

The Hagstrom Family
William J., Sr. and William J., Jr.

The Graber Family
William A., Sr. and William A., Jr.

The Sullivan Family
William B., Clifford P. and Donald G.

The Labanauskas Family
Ignas, Sr. and Ignas G., Jr.

The Scaramella Family
Louis F. and Valerie

The Chronis Family
Basil G. and George B.

The Sylora Family
Herme and James A.

The Cavero Family
Jorge, Sr. and Jorge, Jr.

Our Sisters in Evergreen Park

Little Company Sisters serve all over the world.

Sisters in Evergreen Park, Illinois

Sister Sheila Brosnan, L.C.M.

Sister M. Joseph Casey, L.C.M.

Sister Deborah Conley, L.C.M.

Sister Patricia Dooley, L.C.M.

Sister Mary Jane Feil, L.C.M.

Sister Marianne Herres, L.C.M.

Sister M. Carmelita Hoban, L.C.M.

Sister Margaret Christina Hoban, L.C.M.

Sister Jean Marsden, L.C.M.

Sister Kathleen McIntyre, L.C.M.

Sister Michael Murray, L.C.M.

Sister Virginia O'Brien, L.C.M.

Sister Teresa Oleniczak, L.C.M.

Sister Carol Pacini, L.C.M.

Sister Catherine Shalvey, L.C.M.

Sister Jean Stickney, L.C.M.

Sister Maura Tangney, L.C.M.

Sister Sharon Ann Walsh, L.C.M.

In Memory of our Beloved Little Company of Mary Sisters in Evergreen Park, Illinois

Sister M. Catherine Barrett, L.C.M.
Sister M. Felix Barrett, L.C.M.
Sister M. James Beaupre, L.C.M.
Sister M. Louis Bertrand, L.C.M.
Sister Alice Besancon, L.C.M.
Sister Nancy Boyle, L.C.M.
Sister M. Rita Bracken, L.C.M.
Sister M. Thaddeus Brennan, L.C.M.
Sister M. Cecilia Burgert, L.C.M.
Sister Juliana Callan, L.C.M.
Sister Rita Carroll, L.C.M.
Sister M. Dominica Cekolin, L.C.M.
Sister Lucy Colgan, L.C.M.
Sister M. Christopher Collins, L.C.M.
Sister Margaret Mary Doherty, L.C.M.
Sister M. Ignatius Dooley, L.C.M.
Sister M. Imelda Durkin, L.C.M.
Mother M. Dorothea Dwight, L.C.M.
Sister M. Raphael Dwyer, L.C.M.
Sister M. Peter Flaherty, L.C.M.
Sister M. Philomena Haslem, L.C.M.
Sister M. Joseph Harrison, L.C.M.
Sister M. Rosarii Hassett, L.C.M.
Sister Veronica Henneberry, L.C.M.
Sister M. Solace Hennegan, L.C.M.
Sister M. Elizabeth Hough, L.C.M.
Sister M. Paul Hurtubise, L.C.M.
Sister M. Helena Johnson, L.C.M.
Mother M. Dunstan Kelleher, L.C.M.

Sister Mary Grace King, L.C.M.
Sister Mary Anne Kohler, L.C.M.
Sister M. Leo Lang, L.C.M.
Sister M. de Lourdes Lee, L.C.M.
Mother M. Stanislaus Madigan, L.C.M.
Sister M. Benedicta Mahony, L.C.M.
Sister Ruth Manning, L.C.M.
Sister M. Regina Marshon, L.C.M.
Sister M. Raphael McCarthy, L.C.M.
Sister M. Colette Morrissey, L.C.M.
Sister M. Callista O'Donoghue, L.C.M.
Sister M. Hilda O'Halloran, L.C.M.
Sister M. Bernadette O'Hara, L.C.M.
Sister M. Agnes O'Neill, L.C.M.
Sister M. Camille Plotzke, L.C.M.
Sister M. Regina Powell, L.C.M.
Sister Ruth Putnam, L.C.M.
Sister Rita Ann Rooney, L.C.M.
Sister M. William Scott, L.C.M.
Sister Mary Rose Solano, L.C.M.
Sister M. Barbara Snyder, L.C.M.
Sister M. Mercedes Sorensen, L.C.M.
Sister M. Joseph Sullivan, L.C.M.
Sister M. Eugene Trenner, L.C.M.
Sister M. Francis Thompson, L.C.M.
Sister M. Evangelist Touhey, L.C.M.
Sister M. Dionysius Touhy, L.C.M.
Sister M. Fidelis Ward, L.C.M.
Sister M. Damian Young, L.C.M.

Our Mission Statement

We, the Sisters, Board of Directors, Physicians and Staff of Little Company of Mary Hospital and Health Care Centers, empowered by the Catholic Church and the inspiration of Venerable Mary Potter, the Foundress of the Little Company of Mary, are committed to provide excellence in the ministry of health care.

Rooted in a deep heritage of care and concern for the sick, suffering and dying, we provide a visible witness to Christ today and move forward into the future with moral, compassionate and modern medical services to the community. We will continue to serve the health and wellness needs of all in the Catholic tradition as we strive to enhance the sacredness of life and human dignity.

– CORE VALUES –

Professionalism – Deliver personalized, professional care

Compassion – Create a compassionate environment

Quality – Provide the highest level of quality care

Responsibility – Be financially prudent

Sister Jean Stickney, L.C.M., Carol Andrews, Mary Jo May and Wendy Drynan

Some say Little Company's story is "the best kept secret on the South Side." It has been our privilege and pleasure to compile the memories, stories and feelings of so many people for this commemorative book. From the Sisters' first dream of building a hospital during the Depression until its reality in 1930, and now as we enter a new millennium, their vision remains strong and filled with faith. We are confident that their journey will continue with their companions along the way the – Greater Company of Mary.

Our warm thanks to Maurice Possley, who brought the stories of our Sisters and staff, friends and benefactors to life through his editing skill and eye for detail. To all who jotted a note, made a phone call, sent a picture or shared a story, thank you for helping to tell a very special "Little" story.

Carol Andrews
Wendy Drynan
Mary Jo May
Sister Jean Stickney, L.C.M.